NCRP REPORT No. 107

IMPLEMENTATION OF THE PRINCIPLE OF AS LOW AS REASONABLY ACHIEVABLE (ALARA) FOR MEDICAL AND DENTAL PERSONNEL

Recommendations of the
NATIONAL COUNCIL ON RADIATION
PROTECTION AND MEASUREMENTS

Issued December 31, 1990

National Council on Radiation Protection and Measurements
7910 WOODMONT AVENUE / Bethesda, MD 20814

LEGAL NOTICE

Library of Congress Cataloging-in-Publication Data

National Council on Radiation Protection and Measurements.
 Implementation of the principle of as low as reasonably achievable (ALARA) for medical and dental personnel : recommendations of the National Council on Radiation Protection and Measurements.
 p, cm. — (NCRP report ; no. 107)
 Prepared by the Scientific Committee 46-3 on ALARA Occupationally-Exposed Individuals in Clinical Radiology, under the auspices of the Scientific Committed 46 on Operational Radiation Safety.
 "Issued December 31, 1990."
 Includes bibliographical references and index.
 ISBN 0-929600-15-0
 1. Ionizing radiation—Safety measures. 2. Medical personnel—Diseases—Prevention. 3. Occupational diseases—Prevention. 4. Ionizing radiation—Standards. I. National Council on Radiation Protection and Measurements. Scientific Committee 46-3 on ALARA for Occupationally-Exposed Individuals in Clinical Radiology. II. National Council on Radiation Protection and Measurements. Scientific Committee 46 on Operational Radiation Safety. III. Title. IV. Series.
 [DNLM: 1. Dental Staff. 2. Medical Staff. 3. Occupational Diseases—prevention & control. 4. Radiation Dosage. 5. Radiation Protection—standards. WN 650 N27751]
RA1231.R2N28   1990
363.17'99—dc20
DNLM/DLC
for Library of Congress   90-13673
                                                                      CIP

Preface

This report is part of a series prepared under the auspices of Scientific Committee 46, Operational Radiation Safety. It provides guidance on the process of implementing the "as low as reasonably achievable" (ALARA) principle for the use of radiation by medical and dental personnel. The use of cost-benefit analysis is recommended as a basic method upon which to base ALARA decisions. Examples are provided to illustrate the ALARA principle as a process of optimization and to provide a starting point for the development of individualized ALARA programs. *NCRP Report No. 91, Recommendations on Limits for Exposure to Ionizing Radiation,* calls for the use of reference ranges for occupational exposures. This report recommends the use of 2 reference ranges, one based on individual dose equivalents, and the other based on collective dose equivalent.

Four reports have already been published as part of this series: NCRP Report No. 59, *Operational Radiation Safety Programs*, NCRP Report No. 71, *Operational Radiation Safety—Training*, NCRP Report No. 88, *Radiation Alarms and Access Control Systems*, and NCRP Report No. 105, *Radiation Protection for Medical and Allied Health Personnel.* Under preparation at this time are reports treating radiation safety in the mineral extraction industry, survey instrument calibration, radiation protection records and emergency planning.

In accordance with the recommendations of NCRP Report No. 82, *SI Units in Radiation Protection and Measurements,* as of January, 1990, only SI units are used in the text. Readers needing factors for conversion of SI to conventional units are encouraged to consult Report No. 82.

This report was prepared by Scientific Committee 46-3. Serving on Scientific Committee 46-3 for the preparation of this report were:

Marc Edwards, *Chairman*
St. Luke's Hospital of Kansas City
Kansas City, Missouri

Stewart C. Bushong
Baylor College of Medicine
Houston, Texas

S. Julian Gibbs
Vanderbilt University
Nashville, Tennessee

Glen V. Dalrymple
University of Arkansas
College of Medicine
Little Rock, Arkansas

James G. Kereiakes
University of Cincinnati
Cincinnati, Ohio

Scientific Committee 46 Liaison Member

William R. Hendee,
American Medical Association
Chicago, Illinois

Serving on Scientific Committee 46 on Operational Radiation Safety for the preparation of this report were:

Charles B. Meinhold, *Chairman*
Brookhaven National Laboratory
Upton, New York

Ernest A. Belvin (1983-1987)
Tennessee Valley Authority
Chattanooga, Tennessee

James E. McLaughlin
University of California
Los Angeles, California

W. Robert Casey
Brookhaven National Laboratory
Upton, New York

Thomas D. Murphy
GPU Nuclear Corporation
Parsippany, New Jersey

Robert Catlin
Electric Power Research Institute
Palo Alto, California

David S. Myers (1987-)
Lawrence Livermore
 National Laboratory
Livermore, California

William R. Hendee
American Medical Association
Chicago, Illinois

Keith Schiager
University of Utah
Salt Lake City, Utah

Kenneth R. Kase
University of Massachusetts
Worcester, Massachusetts

Robert G. Wissink
3M Center
St. Paul, Minnesota

Paul L. Ziemer (1983-1990)
Purdue University
West Lafayette, Indiana

NCRP Secretariat

James A. Spahn (1986-1990)
E. Ivan White (1983-1985)
Robert T. Wangemann (1986)

The Council wishes to express its appreciation to the Committee members for the time and effort devoted to the preparation of this report.

Warren K. Sinclair
President

Bethesda, Maryland
5 October 1990

Contents

1. Introduction

1.1 Prologue

The goal of radiation protection is to limit the probability of radiation induced diseases in persons exposed to radiation (somatic effects) and in their progeny (genetic effects) to a degree that is reasonable and acceptable in relation to the benefits from the activities that involve such exposure.

Modern radiation protection practice requires that exposures be kept to levels which are as low as reasonably achievable (ALARA), economic and social factors being taken into account. The implementation of an operational radiation safety program depends not only upon codified recommendations and regulations but also upon the judgements and perceptions of qualified radiation safety personnel. This reliance on qualitative insight is, at present, the preferred method for providing a level of radiation exposure that is as low as reasonably achievable (ALARA) while dealing with uncertainties in the precise nature of low level radiation risks and in the protective measures best suited to a particular situation. From its beginnings, the radiation safety community has recognized the desirability of providing protective measures that not only meet certain exposure limits, but also provide greater protection so far as is "practicable" or "reasonably achievable." The decision as to what is reasonable has been left to the judgement and insight of qualified personnel.

The decision making process should consider both tangible data, such as shielding effectiveness and cost, and less tangible concerns such as impact on the quality of services performed by occupationally exposed personnel.

No set of rules can be sufficiently complete to dictate the correct response to every radiation safety circumstance. This limitation is particularly evident for occupational exposure in medicine and dentistry, where widely disparate working environments, levels of personnel training and institutional resources are involved. Nevertheless, it is important to reaffirm the desirability of providing optimal radiation protection, including effective implementation of the ALARA principle, and to recognize that while the endpoints of optimal radiation protection cannot be described, it is possible to offer

1

considerable guidance on the process of providing optimal radiation protection. This report offers such guidance in connection with occupational exposure of medical and dental personnel, primarily through the discussion of examples intended to illustrate the implementation process and to provide a starting point for individualized ALARA programs. It is left to each institution to adapt this guidance to its own particular circumstances.

1.2 An Overview of ALARA in Radiation Protection

For over thirty years, national and international radiation protection organizations have recommended that, in addition to adherence to specified limits, the concept of "as low as practicable" (ALAP) and "as low as reasonably achievable" (ALARA) should be applied. While the concept of ALARA began as a cautious approach for dealing with uncertain hazards, it was later recognized that a recommendation for some form of ALARA was a necessary consequence of the adoption of a non-threshold, dose-response relationship for the purposes of radiation protection. All non-threshold models dictate that dose reduction always results in a lower probability of harm. These models imply that doses should be "as low as achievable". It is also recognized, however, that the use of radiation can yield direct and indirect benefits to both individuals and populations. Furthermore, not all dose reductions can be achieved with equal ease or resource expenditure. The semantic solution to this problem is to qualify the recommendation such that doses need only be kept to levels which are as low as "reasonably" achievable, or as low as "optimal", in recognition that further reduction below some level cannot be rationally supported, because the intended benefit would not be obtained, or because the cost would be unreasonable.

Difficulties arise in attempting to define precisely what is meant by "low", "reasonably achievable" and "optimal". To facilitate practical implementation, it is necessary to discuss the intentions and meaning of the ALARA recommendation. It is also necessary to avoid inflexible and imperative definitions. Without flexibility, an ALARA recommendation is subtly transformed into a specific limitation which, although possibly easier to regulate, may ultimately defeat the underlying intent of the recommendation. The concept of flexibility suggests that local radiation protection capabilities and practices may sometimes differ significantly from the ideal and that no one solution is universally optimal. To attempt to impose a single endpoint of ALARA could result in higher exposures at institutions that already do better than this "optimum" and higher costs at institutions which do not. In some circumstances, both precision and flexibility can be maintained by formulating ALARA in terms of monetary cost-benefit optimization. In other circumstances, particularly those not easily cast in mathematical terms, the judgement and experience of the radiation protection professional provides the best mechanism to ensure that the recommendation is met. Advisory information on the implementation of ALARA must recognize and address both means.

1.3   The Need for ALARA in Medicine and Dentistry

Persons employed or directly involved with the use of ionizing radiation in medicine and dentistry in the United States are the largest group of occupationally exposed individuals and receive the second largest fraction of occupational collective dose (see Section 3 for a complete discussion). Medical and dental radiation workers are distributed over thousands of institutions and practices, such that any particular workplace will have comparatively few individuals. For the same reason, much of the routine radiation protection service for these workers is the responsibility of persons other than full time professionals in radiation protection. At any particular site, a small number of monitored workers, which provides a weak statistical basis for optimization determination (see Section 4.2.2), and the lack of resources available for radiation protection can hinder the identification of occupational exposure practices that require improvement.

Because of the large number of exposed individuals, it might logically be assumed that the need for improved ALARA practices is greatest in medicine and dentistry. Little empirical evidence is available to support this assumption, in part because of difficulties in quantifying achievement of ALARA and in part because of difficulties in performing properly controlled comparisons. As reviewed in Section 3.3, anecdotal information indicates that individual and collective dose reductions are possible. It should be emphasized, however, that ALARA does not necessarily require dose reductions *per se*. On the other hand, dose reduction that can be achieved with little or no decrease in benefit or increase in cost suggests the need for improved ALARA practices.

1.4 Scope of the Report

This report addresses the implementation of ALARA for occupational exposure of persons working in medicine and dentistry. All applications of ionizing radiation utilized in the normal course of delivering medical and dental health care are included. Experimental and research applications of ionizing radiation are not included. Optimization of exposure to patients undergoing medical and dental procedures is not addressed in this Report. However, there is often a direct relationship between the reduction of exposure to patients and reduction of the exposures of workers. Although reductions in medical exposures consistent with good medical practice are a laudable objective, they deserve consideration in their own right and have been the subject of numerous publications (ICRP, 1982; 1985; 1987). This report is based on the premise that principles and practices of ALARA may be discussed without restating current standards for an operational medical radiation safety program. The purpose of the report is to address the implementation of the principles of ALARA within the context of a pre-existing and properly functioning program, not to address the design of an overall radiation safety program. Refer to NCRP Report No. 59, *Operational Radiation Safety Program* (NCRP, 1978) for recommendations on the design of such a program.

This report is intended for those responsible for radiation protection in any clinical setting. This presents an additional level of difficulty, since the educational background and experience of such individuals are so varied. In a large hospital, radiation protection may be the responsibility of a highly qualified health physicist or medical physicist. Conversely, in a private practice, it may be directed by an individual without such training and experience: a physician (not necessarily a radiologist), dentist, technologist, or administrator. Nevertheless, the aim here is to provide information and recommendations that will be helpful in assuring that occupational exposures are kept to levels which are as low as reasonably achievable.

2. Concepts, Units and Quantities

2.1 Definitions of Units and Quantities

It is important to define the various units and quantities that will be used throughout this report. Among these are those used for the specification of a radiation field (exposure), energy absorbed in a material (absorbed dose), irradiation of an individual (effective dose equivalent), and radioactivity of materials (activity). In the international system (SI) of units, there is no special unit of exposure. Hence, in SI units, exposure is quantified in coulombs per kilogram; 1 R = 2.58×10^{-4} C/kg; 1 C/kg = 3876 R. Because of the awkward conversion factor, it is often convenient to use the concept of air kerma. Kerma is the kinetic energy released in a medium, and has dimensions of energy per unit mass (ICRU, 1980). The special SI unit of kerma is the gray (Gy), where 1 Gy = 1 joule per kilogram. An air kerma of 1 Gy represents a transfer of 1 joule of energy from the x-ray beam to air per kg of air. An exposure of 1 R corresponds to an air kerma of 8.73 mGy (ICRU, 1980). Unless specified otherwise, the term kerma in this report is taken to mean the air kerma in air.

The SI unit of absorbed dose (D) is the gray (Gy); 1 Gy (1 joule of energy absorbed in each kilogram of absorbing material) is equivalent to 100 rad, and 1 rad equals 10 mGy. This unit is not restricted to air and can be measured in other absorbing media (NCRP, 1985).

Dose equivalent (H) is a quantity used for radiation protection purposes. It takes into account both the absorbed dose (D) and the quality factor, Q, for the radiation in question. The special name of the SI unit of dose equivalent is sievert (Sv) (1 sievert = 100 rem). For x rays the dose equivalent is numerically equal to the absorbed dose.

The SI special name for the unit of activity is becquerel (Bq), 1 Bq = 1 s^{-1}. It represents 1 disintegration per second. Since the traditional unit, curie (Ci), which it replaces is 3.7×10^{10} s^{-1}, 1 Ci = 3.7×10^{10} Bq.

A review of traditional units and SI units and their relationships to each other is presented in NCRP Report No. 82 (NCRP, 1985).

5

Absorbed dose is usually taken to be the mean absorbed dose in an organ or tissue. This represents an oversimplification of the actual situation. When an organ or individual is irradiated, the dose is not uniform but is rather inhomogeneous. The use of mean absorbed dose is acceptable based on the assumption that the detriment will be the same whether the irradiation is uniform or nonuniform. The use of the mean dose has practical advantages in that the significant volume can usually be taken as that of the organ or tissue under consideration (ICRP, 1977).

For low doses of radiation delivered to a population, the term collective dose equivalent *(S)* is used. In a given population, this is defined as $S = H_1 P_1$. In this equation, H_1 is the dose equivalent in the whole body or any specified organ, and P_1 represents the number of members in the exposed group.

In an attempt to compare detriment from irradiation of a limited portion of the body with the detriment from irradiation of the total body, the International Commission on Radiological Protection (ICRP, 1977) has derived the concept of effective dose equivalent (H_E), which utilizes weighting factors (w_T) for the relative risks associated with irradiation of various tissues. The effective dose equivalent (H_E) is calculated by adding the products of the dose equivalent and weighting factors for each organ. The weighting factors recommended for use in calculating effective dose equivalent and the risk coefficients from which they were derived are shown in Table 2.1. As defined by the ICRP, the weighting factors are nominal values for an average adult.

2.2 Occupational Exposure and Personnel Dosimetry

In the subsequent chapters of this report, occupational dose equivalents and collective dose equivalents resulting from a variety of situations in the medical workplace are reviewed. The majority of occupational dose equivalent data available in the literature, and reviewed by the NCRP (NCRP, 1989a), is based upon personnel monitoring using individual monitoring devices, such as film or thermoluminescent dosimeters.

There are limitations on the use of personnel dosimetry data for the accurate determinations of effective dose equivalent to individual radiation workers. These limitations are based on three factors, the importance of which depend upon the type of radiation field being measured:

1. orientations of the dosimeter and employee with respect to the radiation field,

TABLE 2.1—*Recommended values of the weighting factors, w_T, for calculating effective dose equivalent and the risk coefficients from which they were derived.*[a]

Tissue (T)	Risk coefficient	w_T
Gonads	40×10^{-4} Sv^{-1}	0.25
Breast	25×10^{-4} Sv^{-1}	0.15
Red bone marrow	20×10^{-4} Sv^{-1}	0.12
Lung	20×10^{-4} Sv^{-1}	0.12
Thyroid	5×10^{-4} Sv^{-1}	0.03
Bone surfaces	5×10^{-4} Sv^{-1}	0.03
Remainder[b]	50×10^{-4} Sv^{-1}	0.30
Total[c]	165×10^{-4} Sv^{-1}	1.00

[a]From NCRP Report No. 91 (NCRP, 1987a).

[b]A w_T of 0.06 is to be assigned to each of the five remainder tissues receiving the highest dose equivalents and the other remainder tissues are to be neglected. (When the gastrointestinal tract is irradiated, the stomach, small intestine, upper large intestine and lower large intestine are to be treated as four separate organs and each may therefore be included in the five remainder tissues depending on the magnitude of the dose equivalent they receive when compared to the dose equivalent received by other remainder tissues and organs.)

[c]The total for somatic risk alone is 125×10^{-4} Sv^{-1} which for radiation protection purposes is often rounded to a nominal value of 1×10^{-2} Sv^{-1}. Genetic risk is 40×10^{-4} Sv^{-1}. For assessment of detriment resulting from exposure of skin, a risk factor of 10^{-4} Sv^{-1} and therefore a weighting factor of 0.01 is to be applied to the mean dose equivalent over the entire skin surface.

2. accuracy of exposure evaluation of the dosimeter under both carefully controlled laboratory conditions and variable field conditions, and

3. relationship of dosimeter measurements to effective dose equivalent.

Personnel dosimeters are designed and used primarily to assure that adequate protection is provided to the wearer and to comply with regulations. Although dosimeters, in varying degrees of sophistication, measure doses which can be converted to dose at various depths in tissue, they are not intended to provide an exclusive measure of organ dose or an accurate measurement of the effective dose equivalent. Additional data concerning the source and exposure conditions are usually required to permit the calculation of the effective dose equivalent.

The International Commission on Radiation Units and Measurements (ICRU) carefully defines effective dose equivalent and the relationship of this quantity to the quantities measured by personnel dosimeters worn on the surface of the body (ICRU, 1985). Ideally, personnel dosimetry data should include information sufficient to enable reasonable estimation (within 30%) of the average and collective dose equivalents; however, published exposure data rarely are sufficiently detailed to enable this to be done. The reason for this need will become clear later in this report when consideration is given to methods for implementation of ALARA (See Section 5). Usually, the reported dose equivalents are the result of conversion of a dosimeter reading to a surface dose equivalent at the point of measurement with simple multiplication by a quantity and/or calibration factor to obtain a dose equivalent which is assigned to the worker and entered in the personnel monitoring record.

It is important to examine the relationship of medical personnel exposure, as recorded by individual monitoring devices, to effective dose equivalent. Exposure to isotropic, high energy photons under conditions that irradiate the entire body (i.e., if no partial body shielding devices such as lead aprons are used) facilitates a straight-forward conversion of monitor data to effective dose equivalent (ICRU, 1988). As will be discussed in Sections 7 and 8, personnel employed in nuclear medicine and radiation therapy are more likely to be exposed to sources that most nearly meet these conditions.

Exposure conditions in diagnostic radiology, particularly those associated with fluoroscopy and special examinations, are more problematic. In these cases, the radiation field is non-uniform, low energy (compared to sources typically encountered in radiation therapy and nuclear medicine) and personnel always use partial body shielding (lead aprons and sometimes thyroid and eye shields). The radiation field is often monitored by a single dosimeter, worn at the collar level outside of protective apparel (Bushong, 1989; Meinhold, 1989). Uncorrected readings from such monitors are not representative of whole body exposure and may not be representative of an organ-dose such as that resulting from an eye exposure. Nevertheless, such placement is more likely to measure the work environment than are other positions. A monitor placed under the protective apron may provide little information about the work environment. Several authors have investigated the relation of monitor readings to effective dose equivalent (Wohni and Stranden, 1979; McGuire et al., 1983; Faulkner and Harrison, 1988; Webster, 1989). Depending on x-ray energy and lead apron thickness, a collar monitor may overestimate effective dose equivalent by factors ranging from 8 to 22 while an under the apron monitor may underestimate effective dose equivalent by factors ranging from 3 to 60 (Faulkner and Harrison, 1988).

From the above discussion it is apparent that, for certain categories of medical workers, effective dose equivalent can be significantly different from figures recorded by individual radiation monitors. Nevertheless, in previous reports on occupational exposure published by the Environmental Protection Agency (EPA, 1984) and the NCRP (NCRP, 1989a), monitoring results were assumed to be representative of effective dose equivalent. The rationale underlying this assumption is that it is impossible to tell from statistical summaries how the monitor was worn, what protective apparel was worn, and how much protection the apparel may have provided. Hence it is impossible to correct the data. Also, for large populations, some errors may tend to cancel if, for instance, some institutions position monitors outside of aprons while others position monitors beneath aprons. *Unless otherwise noted, this report also assumes that personnel exposure for low-LET radiation reported in units of dose equivalent, dose or exposure is representative of effective dose equivalent.*

The NCRP continues to study the problem of finding a practical method for the use of effective dose equivalent in routine personnel monitoring.

3. Characteristics of Occupational Exposure in Medicine and Dentistry

In considering a program for implementing ALARA, it is helpful to examine current data concerning the circumstances and characteristics of medical occupational exposure. This information is useful in its own right because it permits institutions to compare individual situations with national norms. More importantly, the data can be used to identify features of ALARA programs that are applicable to the medical environment.

3.1 Sites of Exposure, Number of Sources and Volume of Procedures

Medical occupational exposure occurs in both hospital and private practice settings. The American Hospital Association identified 5,400 short-term, general, non-federal hospitals, and analyzed radiation-utilizing services as a function of bed size (AHA, 1984). Although not specifically stated in the survey, it is presumed that all of the hospitals had diagnostic x-ray facilities and consequently are sites of medical occupational exposure. Approximately 44 percent of hospitals had fewer than 100 bed capacity while only 6 percent had greater than 500 bed capacity. Sixty-seven percent of all hospitals used diagnostic radionuclides. The more expensive sources of radiation, such as computed tomography and cardiac catheterization facilities are concentrated in the larger hospitals. Data concerning diagnostic imaging in a private practice setting are less accessible and more uncertain. Cook and Nelson (EPA, 1980) estimated that in 1975 there were approximately 49,000 private practice outpatient facilities utilizing diagnostic x rays. The total number of diagnostic x-ray machines in both hospital and private practice settings for the year 1981 was estimated to be 127,000 (NCRP, 1989b). Dental offices are also sites of occupational exposure. In 1980, there were approximately 121,000 dentists in the United States, of whom 90 percent

10

were private practitioners. The number of dental x-ray machines in use in 1981 was estimated to be 204,000 (NCRP, 1989b).

The magnitude of occupational exposure depends not only upon the number of radiation sources but also upon their degree of utilization. The NCRP has extensively reviewed the utilization of medical diagnostic x rays, dental diagnostic x rays and medical radionuclides, hence only a brief overview is required here (NCRP, 1989b). The total number of medical diagnostic x-ray examinations in 1980 was estimated to be 180 million, divided as follows: hospitals, 141 million (78 percent); radiologists' offices, 16 million (9 percent); other physicians offices, 7 million (4 percent); podiatrists, 6 million (3 percent); and chiropractors, 10 million (5.5 percent). The number of dental x-ray procedures in 1980 was estimated to be 101 million. The number of diagnostic radionuclide *in-vivo* examinations in 1982 was estimated to be 7.7 million (NCRP, 1989b).

Radiation therapy sites and number of procedures must be considered separately. The Patterns of Care Study identified 1,083 megavoltage radiation facilities in the United States in 1980, with approximately 378,000 new patients receiving approximately 7.6 million treatments (Kramer *et al.*, 1983). Approximately 80 percent of the facilities were based in non-federal hospitals, 4 percent were based in federal hospitals, 15 percent were freestanding, and the remainder were in unspecified locations. A total of 1,621 megavoltage treatment units, including those both hospital and non-hospital based, were categorized as follows: 820 cobalt-60 units, 762 accelerators and 39 betatrons. Neither the number of superficial and orthovoltage x-ray units nor the number of brachytherapy sources was reported.

3.2 Patterns of Occupational Exposure

Occupational exposure in the United States has been reviewed in NCRP Report No. 101 *Exposure of the U.S. Population from Occupational Radiation* (NCRP, 1989a). The Environmental Protection Agency has also published two reports (EPA, 1980, 1984) that summarized occupational exposure data. Much of the 1984 EPA report, particularly the data on medical occupational exposure, was incorporated into Report No. 101 (NCRP, 1989a). Because detailed data are available in these references, only a brief overview of the portions relevant to medical occupational exposure is needed here.

In 1980 there were approximately 584,000 "medical" workers. In this case, the term "medical" workers encompasses hospital, private practice, dental, podiatry, chiropractic and veterinary workers. Of these 584,000 workers, all of whom were potentially exposed to radiation, approximately 277,000 received a yearly exposure exceeding the minimum detectable limit (MDL). Those workers receiving greater than the MDL are denoted as "measurably exposed". The mean annual whole body dose equivalent of all medical workers was 0.70 mSv/y while for measurably exposed medical workers it was 1.5 mSv/y. The annual collective dose equivalent was 410 person-Sv. The NCRP has reviewed the problems inherent in calculating effective whole body dose equivalent from monitoring data. However, no attempt has been made to correct these figures for partial body exposure or the use of shielding devices such as lead aprons (NCRP, 1989a).

Trends for mean annual dose equivalent and collective dose equivalent for all categories of workers over the time period 1960 to 1980 have been reviewed (NCRP, 1989a). The data reveal that, while collective dose equivalent has increased with time, the mean annual dose equivalent has decreased. Until 1980, the exposure of medical workers yielded the largest fraction of collective dose. In 1980, nuclear fuel cycle workers exceeded medical workers in collective dose equivalent for the first time; this group is expected to be the largest occupational contributor to collective dose equivalent in the future. The medical occupational subgroup has shown a decrease of approximately 50 person-Sv every five years since 1960, despite an increase in the number of potentially exposed medical personnel by approximately 18 percent every five years. This decrease in occupational collective dose equivalent from medical sources is due to a reduction in the mean annual dose to medical workers by approximately 20 percent every five years.

A more detailed exposition of the number of medical workers and their collective dose equivalent contributions by specialty group for 1980 is shown in Table 3.1 (EPA, 1984). The contributions from podiatry, chiropractic and veterinary practices account for less than five percent of the medical collective dose equivalent. Hospital, private practice and dental workers constitute the greatest number of occupationally exposed workers; primarily because of their large numbers, these groups contribute the largest fraction of (medical) collective dose equivalent. Dental workers, whose numbers are nearly as great as that of hospital and private practice combined, received a much smaller annual per caput dose equivalent and hence account for only 14 percent of the medical collective dose equivalent.

An additional important descriptor of occupational exposure is the frequency distribution of dose equivalent. Data for the total medical workforce, including all potentially exposed workers both monitored and unmonitored, are shown in Table 3.2 (EPA, 1984). These data,

TABLE 3.1—*National occupational exposure summary of medical workers for 1980 (EPA, 1984).*

Occupational subgroup	Number of workers[a]		Mean annual whole-body dose[a] (mSv)		Annual collective dose[a] (person-Sv)
	Total[b]	Exposed[c]	Total	Exposed	
Hospital	126,000	86,000	1.40	2.00	172
Private practice	155,000	87,000	1.00	1.80	160
Dental	259,000	82,000	0.20	0.70	56
Podiatry	8,000	3,000	0.10	0.30	1
Chiropractic	15,000	6,000	0.30	0.80	5
Veterinary	21,000	12,000	0.60	1.10	13
ENTIRE SUBGROUP	584,000	276,000	0.70	1.50	407

[a]Numbers of workers are estimated values and are rounded to nearest thousand. Mean doses are rounded to the nearest 0.1 mSv, and collective doses to the nearest person-Sv.

[b]All monitored and unmonitored workers with potential occupational exposure.

[c]Workers who received a measurable dose in any monitoring period during the year.

TABLE 3.2—*Dose equivalent and collective dose frequency distribution by dose range for the 1980 medical radiation workforce.*[a]

Dose equivalent range (mSv/y)	Number of workers	Percent of workers	Collective dose (person-Sv)	Percent of collective dose
0–MD	306506	52.5	8.50	2.1
MD–1	205969	35.3	68.43	16.8
1–2.5	36078	6.2	61.21	15.0
2.5–5.0	18284	3.1	59.52	14.6
5–10	10324	1.8	66.55	16.4
10–20	4629	0.79	65.62	16.1
20–30	1321	0.23	32.73	8.0
30–40	467	0.08	18.36	4.5
40–50	217	0.04	9.85	2.4
50–80	205	0.04	12.69	3.1
80–120	40	0.007	3.54	0.9
120+	0	0	0	0

[a]The data include both exposed and potentially exposed workers for all occupational subgroups given in Table 3.1. A large portion of the workers in the O–MD (Minimum Detectable) range are dental workers. Each occupational subgroup follows the same type of distribution but with a different mean (EPA, 1984).

like most other occupational dose equivalent distributions, illustrate several typical features. First, the distribution is heavily skewed toward low annual dose equivalents. Although the average annual dose equivalent was about 0.7 mSv/y for the total potentially exposed workforce, approximately 53 percent of the group received less than measurable dose equivalent and 88 percent received less than 1 mSv/y. Of the exposed workers (those receiving a measurable dose equivalent at least once during the year), whose average annual dose equivalent was about 1.5 mSv/y, approximately 75 percent received less than 1 mSv/y. Second, the largest contribution to collective dose equivalent is made by the small fraction of workers who receive high dose equivalents. The 3 percent of the total workforce (6 percent of the exposed group) who receive an annual dose equivalent greater than 5 mSv/y contribute approximately 51 percent of the collective dose equivalent. Finally, in 1980 less than 0.5 percent of the total workforce received an annual dose equivalent in excess of 20 mSv/y and less than 0.05 percent received an annual dose equivalent in excess of the recommended upper limit of 50 mSv/y.

As discussed in NCRP Report No. 101 (NCRP, 1989a), dose equivalent distributions for many categories of occupational exposure have been shown to be reasonably well approximated by the log-normal distribution. This mathematical expression states that the logarithm of annual dose equivalent is distributed according to the normal probability function. The log-normal distribution can be helpful in estimating the contribution of less than measurable doses to the collective dose. However, Cook and Nelson found only a 3 percent difference by using the log-normal distribution compared to setting the collective dose of that group equal to zero (EPA, 1980).

Average annual dose equivalent, taken alone, is not a sufficient descriptor of success or failure of radiation protection efforts because it is highly dependent on the large numbers of monitored workers receiving less than the minimum detectable value for the monitoring device used. Annual collective dose, although essential for estimating detriment, is dependent on the number of workers and their workload. One parameter that describes the efficiency of "expenditure" of occupational exposure in the attainment of a production level is the ratio of annual collective dose to annual workload. A lower ratio implies better radiation protection. This type of analysis has been attempted for diagnostic x-ray facilities in various countries (UNSCEAR, 1982). Workload was measured as the number of films used for x-ray examinations per year, with the result that the collective dose per film ranged from 0.5×10^{-2} to 4.2×10^{-6} person-Sv/film. Similar factors can be calculated using procedure volume rather than number of films to estimate workload. Kumazawa *et al.* indicated that hospital-based personnel received a collective dose of 172 person-Sv in 1980 (see Table 3.1) (EPA, 1984). The data of Johnson and Abernathy indicated that in 1980 there were 151×10^6 hospital-based imaging procedures using radiation (Johnson and Abernathy, 1983). Thus, the collective dose per procedure is approximately 1.1×10^{-6} person-Sv/procedure. This figure is somewhat misleading, however, because radiation therapy operations (particularly brachytherapy) contribute to collective dose but were not counted in procedure volume. A more meaningful approach would be to acquire data on collective dose per unit workload of each area having a unique occupational subgroup (see Section 8).

3.3 Is There Evidence of Need for Improved ALARA Practices?

In the previous section, it was shown that there are good reasons for believing that individual dose limitations are rarely exceeded by medical workers. It is a much more difficult task to either prove or disprove the conjecture that medical occupational exposure is as low as reasonably achievable. To demonstrate the need for improvement in radiation protection, an analysis should reveal that either the cost of radiation protection or the cost of radiation detriment, or both, could be reduced while the net benefit to society of the use of radiation could be improved or at least maintained. Potential for reduction of average dose or collective dose is, by itself, not sufficient to indicate the desirability of modified radiation safety practices.

Many of the reports that have been cited as indications of practices incompatible with the utilization of the ALARA concept are anecdotal in nature and often do not address the issues of cost and benefit. Several authors have reported a reduction in exposure of nuclear medicine personnel per unit work load over a several year period (Barrall and Smith, 1976; Gandsman et al., 1980). Although the cost of the dose reduction measures was not discussed, many of the measures involved simple changes in operational procedures that would not be expected to incur major expense. Reduction in the average whole body exposure of nuclear medicine personnel as a result of the operation of a Nuclear Pharmacy has also been reported (Ahluwalia et al., 1981). Effects on collective dose and operating cost were not discussed. A review of fourteen years of personnel radiation exposure in a radiation oncology facility revealed a trend toward decreasing collective dose and decreasing average annual dose (Leung, 1983). However, no major operational changes occurred during the time period, and no special effort was made to optimize exposures other than normal practices of radiation protection. The EPA has partially ascribed dose reductions, particularly reductions in the number of personnel exceeding 50 mSv/y, to ALARA regulatory requirements (EPA, 1984). However, the trend in U.S. medical collective dose has been steadily downward ever since reliable data first became available in 1960. It seems equally plausible to conclude that the original "ALAP" recommendation was being observed before any additional regulations were promulgated, although regulated changes in medical equipment, such as minimum filtration requirements, beam collimation and exposure rate limits, could also be contributing factors. Non-regulated changes, such as faster intensifying screens, more image intensified fluoroscopes and better trained personnel may be of equal, if not greater, importance.

To summarize, there is no conclusive evidence of the need for improved ALARA practices but there is also no reason to assume that, unless the ALARA principle is applied, all workers are being provided the maximum protection possible.

4.   The ALARA Requirement

4.1   Cost-Benefit Analysis

4.1.1   *Background and Historical Review*

The basic principle known as ALARA has been an integral part of the overall philosophy of radiation protection for over forty years. As reviewed by Auxier and Dickson (1983), the ALARA concept traces its beginnings to the radiation protection programs of the Manhattan Project. The NCRP recommended in 1954 that radiation exposure should "be kept at the lowest practical level" (NCRP, 1954). The International Commission on Radiological Protection (ICRP) made a similar recommendation in 1959 (ICRP, 1959). All subsequent recommendations of the NCRP and ICRP have endorsed the principle of ALARA, as originally conceived although with differing terminology and differing degrees of explanation.

NCRP recommendations concerning ALARA were discussed in *Basic Radiation Protection Criteria*, NCRP Report No. 39 (NCRP, 1971) and subsequently reviewed in *Review of the Current State of Radiation Protection Philosophy*, NCRP Report No. 43 (NCRP, 1975). [Both superseded by Report No. 91 (NCRP, 1987a), discussed below.] The general principle governing occupational exposure espoused by the NCRP at that time was that, since no inflexible numerical criteria governing radiation exposure could be given, modifications of the recommended maximum permissible values might be justified on the basis of social, technical, and economic factors. Because a non-threshold dose-effect relationship was assumed, all radiation exposure was to be held to the lowest practicable level. The particular levels compatible with the term "lowest practicable" must be site-specific, and determined according to acceptable risk (NCRP, 1971). The NCRP noted that the establishment of radiation protection standards requires consideration of trade-offs between hazards and benefits (NCRP, 1975, p. 2). Identification and quantification of both risks and benefits were considered so uncertain at that time that the practice of balancing risks and benefits numerically could not be pursued. However, the risk-benefit approach was important "in order to avoid the expenditure of large amounts of the limited resources of

17

society to reduce very small risks still further with possible concomitant increase in risks of other hazards or consequent lack of attention to existing greater risks" (NCRP, 1975, p. 3).

The International Commission on Radiological Protection (ICRP) has recommended a philosophy of radiation protection based upon quantitative risk. The basic system was set forth in *Recommendations of the ICRP*, ICRP Publication 26 (ICRP, 1977, p. 2, 3):

"Most decisions about human activities are based on an implicit form of balancing of costs and benefits leading to the conclusion that the conduct of a chosen practice is "worthwhile". Less generally, it is also recognized that the conduct of the chosen practice should be adjusted to maximize the benefit to the individual or to society. In radiation protection, it is becoming possible to formalize these broad decision-making procedures, though not always to quantify them....

The Commission recommends a system of dose limitation, the main features of which are as follows:

(a) no practice shall be adopted unless its introduction produces a positive net benefit;

(b) all exposures shall be kept as low as reasonably achievable, economic and social factors being taken into account; and

(c) the dose equivalent to individuals shall not exceed the limits recommended for the appropriate circumstances by the Commission."

The ICRP has stated that the recommendation for ALARA is synonymous with a recommendation for "optimization of radiation protection". Because the ICRP system is based upon quantitative risk and detriment, it facilitates a quantitative description of the ALARA (optimization) recommendation based upon cost-benefit considerations. This approach was explored in considerable detail in ICRP Publication 37, *Cost-Benefit Analysis in the Optimization of Radiation Protection* (ICRP, 1983). The report recognizes that quantitative techniques have both strengths and weaknesses (ICRP, 1983, p. 2, 3):

"Optimization of radiation protection applies to all situations where radiation exposures can be controlled by protection measures. . . . . The degree of quantification in the techniques used for radiation protection optimization will vary with the different applications. Designers of installations and protection systems will tend to use more quantitative techniques for deciding the degree of protection (shielding thickness, containment, ventilation rates, etc.) that will meet the optimization require-ment. Competent authorities may use stylized quantitative techniques of optimization in deriving appropriate authorized limits and requirements for given types of installations, radia-tion sources or practices involving radiation exposures.

Optimization of radiation protection during operations usu-ally, but not necessarily always, tends to be less quantitative. . . . . Quantitative assessments of radiation pro-tection optimization are not suggested for daily operational practice. The persons responsible for radiation protection in daily operations will have to follow simpler rules imposed by the competent authority or the management, on the basis of the optimization principle. In addition, they may be guided by the general ambition of optimizing radiation protection, although in an intuitive rather than quantitative way."

Radiation protection optimization was cast as decision analysis, with cost-benefit analysis offering a quantitative technique for calcu-lating decision criteria. The ICRP approach will be discussed in further detail as parts of Sections 4.1.2 to 4.1.4.

Current NCRP recommendations concerning ALARA are con-tained in *Recommendations on Limits for Exposure to Ionizing Radia-tion*, NCRP Report 91 (NCRP, 1987a), superseding the previous Reports 39 and 43. The NCRP has endorsed the "previous recommen-dations concerning: (1) the need to justify any activity which involves radiation exposure on the basis that the expected benefits exceed the predicted cost (justification), (2) the need to reduce the total radiation detriment from such justifiable activities or practices to as low a level as is reasonably achievable (ALARA), economic and social factors being taken into account, and (3) the need to apply individual effective dose equivalent limits to ensure that the procedures for justification and ALARA do not result in individuals or groups of individuals exceeding acceptable levels of risk" (NCRP, 1987a, p.5). The NCRP also recognizes that optimization, as defined in ICRP Publication 37, has the same meaning as ALARA.

4.1.2 *Risk Models and Minimization of Exposure*

The relationship between dose and effect is an essential part of the basis for guidelines for the safe utilization of any hazardous agent. Although radiation effects have been extensively studied for over six decades, considerable uncertainty still exists about their precise functional form and magnitude, particularly for human populations exposed to the dose ranges encountered in typical radiation protection circumstances. This uncertainty is due primarily to the small probability of the effects occurring. To deal with the uncertainty, dose-effect models have been developed that reflect both the best available data and the applications for which the models are to be used.

As discussed in the BEIR III Report (NAS/NRC, 1980), several different dose-effect models that describe known high dose data equally well yield greatly different predictions in the low dose region. Although the linear model has been neither proved nor disproved to be the most accurate model for predicting low level radiation effects in human populations, it is often used for radiation protection purposes. This is because there is some (but not conclusive) evidence supporting its factual validity, because it is perceived to be a "conservative" model which, if anything, overestimates the effects of low level, low LET radiation, and because it is compatible with the concept of collective dose.

Rather than the general term "radiation effect", the more precise terms of "risks", and "detriment" are preferred. Following ICRP terminology, "risk" is defined as the probability that a given individual will incur a particular radiation-induced effect as a result of the dose received, while "detriment" is the probability of harm induced in an exposed group of people, taking into account both the probability and severity of all possible harmful effects (ICRP, 1983). That is, risk and detriment are measures of probability, not certainty. Probabilistic models can predict the fraction of a population that will be harmed by exposure, but they cannot predict which particular members of the population will experience the harm. The ICRP quantifies risk and detriment using the linear model as follows: If a population receives a collective dose equivalent S (person-Sv), the health detriment, G, for that population is given by

$$G = RS, \qquad (4.1)$$

where R is the total risk (serious effects/dose equivalent). The value of R has been taken to be 1.65×10^{-2} Sv^{-1}, of which 1.25×10^{-2} Sv^{-1} is for fatal cancers and 0.4×10^{-2} Sv^{-1} is due to serious hereditary effects in the first two generations (ICRP, 1983). These estimates of risk may be increased in the future as recent epidemiological data, especially for the survivors of the A bombs in Japan, indicate (UNSCEAR, 1988). This expected increase was already noted by NCRP (NCRP, 1987a) and will be fully discussed in relation to radiation protection in a forthcoming report (NCRP, 1991a) (Report of Scientific Committee 1-2).

All non-threshold models state that risk and detriment can be reduced to zero only when the dose equivalent is zero. Although there may be a "risk free" level of radiation, and although the magnitudes of risks and detriments of radiation levels encountered in radiation protection are very small, it is still conservatively assumed that there is no "absolutely risk free" level of radiation, at least for the purposes of radiation protection. From these considerations, it follows that maximum radiation protection can be achieved only by the minimization of exposure. The problem with this approach is its tacit assumption that low level radiation is the only risk to which a worker is exposed and that minimization is desirable regardless of the cost of resources expended. The principle of ALARA addresses these major issues.

4.1.3 *Optimization of Radiation Protection*

A level of radiation protection that is ALARA implies neither maximum protection nor maximum resource expenditure, but rather that detriments and resource expenditures have been optimized to yield the greatest net benefit. As more resources are expended, benefits are gained due to decreased health detriment; at the same time, benefits are lost due to the depletion of resources. In many cases, an optimal resource expenditure level exists which, if either increased or decreased, results in a decrease in net benefit. This defines the optimal level of radiation protection. All recommended systems of radiation protection require that the optimal level of protection shall not result in any dose equivalent limitation being exceeded. Hence, the optimization process is utilized only for exposures below limit values.

Although the optimization process is more easily conceptualized as a mathematical procedure, other procedures may be used. In circumstances for which no precise quantitative relationship between benefit and resource expenditure can be derived, optimization necessarily proceeds in a qualitative fashion, with estimates of net benefit based upon experience, intuition and value judgement. Qualitative optimization is not a "blank check" to select arbitrarily any level of protection. Just as the decisions of a trial judge must be logical, defensible and within legal precedent, so must the decisions concerning the optimal level of radiation protection be logical, defensible and within precedents established by the radiation protection community.

If the relationship between net-benefit and resource expenditure can be exactly quantified, then the decision-making process reduces to the solution of a set of equations, and the laws of mathematics become the impartial judge of the optimal solution. The cost-benefit model of optimization is such a system. As will be seen below, there are relatively few circumstances that may be reduced to a set of equations. Nevertheless, the cost-benefit model provides an important conceptual guide for the optimization process.

4.1.4. *The Cost-Benefit Model of Optimization*

The cost-benefit model of optimization assumes that a precise mathematical relationship exists between benefits and resources, and that net benefit can be expressed in monetary terms. The net benefit B from the utilization of radiation is expressed as $B = V-(P+X+Y)$, where V is the gross benefit resulting from that utilization, P is the production cost excluding the cost of radiation protection, X is the cost of radiation protection and Y is the cost of radiation detriment. Most optimization calculations assume that V, the gross benefit, and P, the production cost excluding the cost of radiation protection, are not affected by radiation protection decisions. Hence, maximum benefit occurs when the sum of the costs of radiation protection and radiation detriment is minimized:

$$X[\$] + Y[\$] = \text{minimum.} \tag{4.2}$$

The cost of achieving a given level of protection is denoted by $X[\$]$. This cost includes both capital costs and subsequent operating costs of radiation protection over the expected lifetime of the system. Various degrees of sophistication of cost estimation, including crude costs, present worth and capitalized cost, have been suggested by the ICRP. The ultimate result of a cost-benefit optimization can be affected by the choice of accounting methodology used to assess either cost or detriment. Another complication, referred to as the "distributional problem" by the ICRP (ICRP, 1983, p. 21), is that different individuals or populations may bear the cost, suffer the detriment or receive the benefit of a particular application of radiation. An example might be an employer who incurs higher radiation protection costs to reduce the risk of genetic detriment, the benefit of which is received not by the employer or employees but by their future generations. In a formal cost-benefit optimization, problems of this nature must be accounted for in monetary terms.

The monetary cost of the objective health detriment, $Y[\$]$, is related to the collective effective dose equivalent by

$$Y[\$] = \alpha[\$/\text{person-Sv}]S[\text{person-Sv}], \tag{4.3}$$

where α is a constant expressing the cost assigned to the unit collective dose, S, for radiation protection purposes. Subjective factors, such as psychological response to exposure, societal desire to avoid radiation risk in a manner disproportionate compared to other risks, or a desire to obtain public or worker goodwill by providing greater radiation protection than is otherwise warranted, may also be included as "subjective detriment" (ICRP, 1983). Because subjective detriment is not based on biological response, its dependence on dose equivalent is problematic. The ICRP gives several examples of optimization that explicitly include the monetary cost of subjective detriment (ICRP, 1983). In this report, only the objective health detriment is explicitly considered. The value of α is, in principle, related to objective health detriment, as discussed by the ICRP (ICRP, 1983, p. 19):

> "The risk factors . . . allow for the prediction of the most important health effects that can result from exposure to radiation. These factors, coupled with the collective dose commitment concept, can give a statistical prediction of the number of cancers and serious hereditary effects occurring as a result of a practice. If, by some means, it were possible to assign a monetary value to these stochastic health effects, then the value of α would approximately be equal to that value divided by the relevant risk factor for fatal cancer induction as a result of whole-body irradiation. This procedure has considerable appeal because it could lead to a consistent application in a variety of different situations. . . . . However, any valuation is of statistical lives, and not of particular individuals; for example, although the value of the change in life expectancy of unknown individuals is actually being assessed, no value is being assigned to identified individuals."

In its most basic form, cost-benefit optimization thus seeks to find a solution to the equation

$$X + \alpha S = \text{minimum.} \qquad (4.4)$$

A particularly simple example occurs when considering a discrete change in protection from some level A to a more costly level B. If the non-objective costs can be ignored, such a change is indicated if

$$-\frac{X_B - X_A}{S_B - S_A} \leq \alpha. \qquad (4.5)$$

This expression states that the additional cost expended per person-Sv collective dose reduction should be less than the value established for α. For complex systems involving multiple parameters with interrelated subsystems, the mathematics of formal optimization becomes complex, requiring sophisticated computational techniques for solution.

Cost-benefit optimization is most feasible in circumstances involving a single variable that is related in a straightforward manner to cost and collective dose. These circumstances are most likely to occur in the radiation protection design of facilities. The ICRP gives specific numerical examples of optimizing the thickness of a barrier, the ventilation flow rate and environmental release of radioactive materials. The ICRP shows, for example, that the optimal amount of shielding to be added to a barrier wall already in compliance with dose limit recommendations is given by the solution to the equation (ICRP, 1983, p. 29)

$$e^{-\Gamma w_o} = \frac{X_v hl}{\tau \alpha \Gamma \dot{H}_\mu f_t N_\rho} \tag{4.6}$$

where

w_o = optimized extra shield thickness,
Γ = effective attenuation coefficient of the shielding material,
X_v = cost per unit volume of the shielding material (shielding cost assumed to be directly proportional to volume of shielding material),
h = shield height,
l = shield length,
τ = lifetime of the installation,
α = cost assigned per unit collective dose,
$\dot{H}_\mu$ = maximum effective dose-equivalent rate at contact with wall,
f_t = occupancy time factor,
N = number of exposed individuals, and
ρ = ratio between average and maximum dose rates.

The total shield thickness is then equal to the sum of the initial thickness plus the extra thickness. Detailed calculations, including numerical examples, are given in ICRP Publication 37 (ICRP, 1983).

Formal cost-benefit optimization of radiation protection operations is more difficult than optimization of facility design. Radiation protection operations are dependent on human factors such as the training and competence of personnel, quality of management and operational instructions and diligence of compliance with operational instructions. Consequently, it is difficult to quantify both the costs and detriments associated with a given operation. The ICRP concludes that "the optimization process in operations can seldom be complete, a situation that renders decisions about alternative operational procedures largely qualitative and intuitive, with a substantial component of non-quantitative value judgement" (ICRP, 1983, p. 36).

4.2. Difficulties Presented by the Cost-Benefit Model of Optimization

4.2.1 General Difficulties

A significant obstacle to the actual utilization of cost-benefit optimization for implementation of ALARA, in both exact and intuitive situations, is the numerical definition of α, the monetary value assigned per unit collective dose. As previously discussed, the monetary basis of cost-benefit analysis requires a monetary valuation of statistical life because detriment is quantified in terms of statistical death. However, no universally accepted method to arrive at such a valuation has been identified. The ICRP reviewed some of the proposed techniques, including legal damages, insurance premiums, loss of national income and health and social care expenses due to the death of an average worker. Values obtained by these techniques ranged from $1,000 to $100,000 per person-Sv. In numerical examples the ICRP used a value of $10,000 per person-Sv without recommending that this particular value had any merit over some other value (ICRP, 1983).

4.2.2 Difficulties Unique to the Medical Environment

The unusual circumstances of the medical environment can have a significant impact on occupational exposure. Measures to modify radiation protection practices that could easily be taken in other occupations may not be feasible in medicine because of their impact on patient care. For example, proximity to a patient may be necessary during a radiation procedure to perform the examination. The benefit to the patient should always be a major consideration when analyzing medical radiation protection. Of course, it is difficult to assign a numerical value to patient benefit or to compare patient benefit to occupational worker benefit.

While the conceptual framework of the implementation of ALARA as cost-benefit optimization can be well supported in theory, many problems arise in practical application of this concept in a medical setting. Formal optimization is best suited to facility design problems. Although there is some evidence to indicate that a moderate fraction of medical exposure is due to inadequacy of shielding [primarily syringe shields (Branson et al., 1976) and portable barriers (Brateman et al., 1979; Kosnik and Meengs, 1986)], most reports of dose reduction cite operational change as a major cause of improvement. In those situations amenable to formal optimization, the problem of assigning a value to α remains. Until there is a nationally agreed upon value for α, the radiation safety committee of each institution would have to agree upon a value which, presumably, would fall within the inflation- adjusted range discussed by the ICRP.

The responsibility for radiation protection of medical workers is widely dispersed. At a particular site, responsibility may often be entrusted to personnel with many other clinical or administrative duties. From the data discussed in Section 3 it is evident that there are tens of thousands of sites using medical radiation. Each site involves a comparatively small number of exposed or potentially exposed workers. Thus, situations are likely to arise in which personnel untrained in the technique of cost benefit analysis might experience difficulty in implementing the concept.

Having few employees per site also presents difficulties in confirming the success or failure of a radiation protection program, because the indicators of effective radiation protection practice are more susceptible to statistical imprecision when few data points are available. Small samples are difficult to interpret. In this situation, questions arise as to whether a few data points falling outside the normal range are sufficient evidence to warrant an expenditure of resources to reduce radiation exposure. Conversely, the absence of data points outside of the normal range may not necessarily indicate the successful maintenance of radiation exposures "as low as reasonably achievable".

4.3 Reference Levels in Optimization

In principle, all aspects of the radiation safety program should be reviewed to provide optimal individual and collective dose equivalent. This would entail a constant awareness of sources of exposure, the manner in which exposure is received, ongoing consideration of cost effective strategies for modification of individual and collective dose equivalents, and periodic review and reappraisal of the effectiveness of training, procedures, facilities and equipment to ensure that the optimum is being achieved. This approach is unfocussed, in that it considers all facets of the radiation protection program on an equal basis. Yet, some facets may benefit more from optimization than others. Furthermore, the method through which fulfillment of the ALARA requirement is demonstrated, *i.e.,* showing that any change in design or operation of the entire department would result in greater cost or greater detriment, may require a great deal of effort. Such a global approach, while desirable, may be beyond the resources of many medical institutions. In these circumstances, it may be satisfactory to limit the range of optimization activities based upon radiation monitoring records of occupationally exposed individuals. In order to accomplish this, upper and lower boundaries of exposure must be defined to focus the scope of optimization activities.

The upper limit used for implementing ALARA is determined by recommended or mandated dose-equivalent limits (*i.e.*, 50 mSv/y annual whole body and/or other organ-specific and population specific limits as set by the NCRP or ICRP). The symbol D_{LIM} is used to denote a recommended dose equivalent limit. The lower boundary of ALARA activities is determined by the "negligible individual risk level" (NIRL), defined by the NCRP as that annual individual dose equivalent below which the average excess risk of health detriment is so low as to make unwarranted any further effort to reduce individual exposure (NCRP, 1987a). Dose equivalents below the NIRL need not be considered for optimization or any other protective measures. The NCRP has set the numerical value of the NIRL to be 0.01 mSv/y (NCRP, 1987a). The NIRL applies to all individuals, both occupationally exposed and members of the public, and applies to all aspects of radiation protection including facility design and operations management.

The range of individual exposures subject to optimization thus lies between the NIRL and the D_{LIM} values. In the case of occupationally exposed personnel, this range of dose equivalents encompasses nearly everyone since D_{LIM} is rarely exceeded. Hence, it is desirable to refine further the scope of optimization such that activities are concentrated on individuals for whom the greatest reduction is likely to be achieved. One method for attaining such a refinement is the use of "reference levels" or "action levels".

The term "reference level" (used by the NCRP) or "action level" (used by the ICRP) denotes a site-specific and predetermined level of dose equivalent or collective dose which, if reached, initiates a predetermined course of action. The reference level is a single value of dose equivalent that divides inaction from action. In the case of the occupationally exposed medical personnel, variable exposure patterns and monitoring data make it difficult to assign a single number to the reference level. Instead, a fairly broad "reference range" may be used. As with the reference level, dose equivalents falling above or below the reference range do or do not initiate action. However, dose equivalents falling within the reference range are in a "gray area" that requires more consideration. The reference range for occupationally exposed individuals may be established by examining the properties of the distribution of occupational exposure over the population of monitored individuals.

A graph of cumulative percent of workers and cumulative percent of collective dose equivalent versus dose equivalent is shown in Figure 4.1. The data are taken from Table 3.2 for workers receiving greater than minimum detectable dose equivalent during the year. The mean annual dose equivalent for these workers measurably exposed is approximately 1.5 mSv/y. As discussed in Section 3.2, dose equivalent distributions for medical and dental personnel are approximated by the log-normal probability function. Hence, the data of Figure 4.1 are representative of dose equivalent distributions of many categories and subcategories of workers; the functional dependence remains the same (log-normal) but the mean annual dose equivalent depends upon the particular category of workers. In general, the NIRL defines the lower bound of the dose equivalent scale. The upper bound of the dose equivalent scale is D_{LIM}, which in this case is 50 mSv. The reference range (IRR) divides the dose

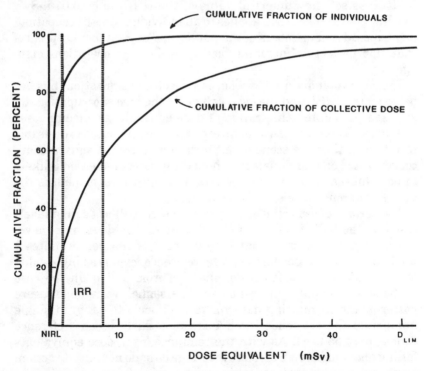

Fig. 4.1 Representative plot of the cumulative fraction of individuals and the cumulative fraction of collective dose versus dose equivalent. See text for explanation. IRR is the individual reference range.

equivalent scale into three regions: dose equivalents above the NIRL but below the reference range; dose equivalents within the reference range (IRR); and dose equivalents above the reference range but below D_{LIM}. These regions are used to determine the scope and intensity of optimization activities.

The Individual Reference Range (IRR) is defined as that range of individual dose equivalent values that, if exceeded, automatically triggers optimization activity. Hence, all individual dose equivalents above the IRR must be reviewed and actions taken to reduce the exposure from the identified procedure to as low as reasonably achievable. The IRR is not a dose limitation because in certain instances an exposure exceeding the IRR may already be optimal and hence should not be modified. However, it is desirable to concentrate effort on those measures that affect exposures exceeding the IRR. This is because only a few individuals are expected to exceed the IRR, thus focussing the scope of ALARA activities; and because these individuals represent the greatest potential for collective dose equivalent reduction, assuming individual dose equivalent is not reduced by averaging over more workers. Each institution should set its own IRR depending upon its experience and radiation protection philosophy. As a general guideline, the upper bound of the IRR should be greater than the average dose, but not set so high that it is rarely exceeded. A properly set upper bound would be expected to be exceeded by a few percent of workers during the course of several review periods. In the example shown in Figure 4.1, the upper bound of the IRR is exceeded by approximately 1 percent of all potentially exposed workers and by 5 percent of measurably exposed workers. However, the group of workers with doses above the IRR contributes approximately 40 percent of the collective dose equivalent. The upper bound of the IRR thus identifies individuals for whom ALARA activities would have the greatest potential value.

The lower bound of the IRR defines the individual exposure below which no optimization activity need be initiated. Although "reasonable" dose reductions may be possible for individuals with doses below the IRR, the potential for collective dose reduction from these individuals is small, even considering the large number of individuals in the group. However, additional consideration is given to this group in terms of the collective reference range, to be discussed below. *It should be emphasized that elimination of individuals receiving dose equivalents between the NIRL and IRR from automatic optimization action does not imply that cost effective dose reduction efforts should not be undertaken for this group. If a cost effective measure is known, it should be implemented regardless of the dose levels of the individuals affected.* The purpose of the reference range is to limit the scope of new optimization investigations based upon the potential return in collective dose reduction. As a general guideline, the lower bound of the IRR should be set high enough to exclude a large fraction of individuals from optimization without encompassing a significant fraction of collective dose. In the example shown in Figure 4.1, the lower bound of the IRR has been set above the exposures of approximately 90 percent of potentially exposed workers and 80 percent of measurably exposed workers. The group of workers excluded from consideration by the lower bound of the IRR contributes only 25 percent of the total collective dose. If the distribution of dose equivalent does not follow the expected log-normal distribution, the bounds of the IRR may be adjusted to ensure that the fraction of individuals excluded is not too large.

Individual exposures falling within the IRR are left to the discretion of the institutional radiation safety authority. A consistent history of exposure in this region may indicate a need to initiate optimization activity, whereas an occasional reading would cause less concern. A group of individuals engaged in the same activity and all receiving exposures in this region, rather than a broad range of exposures, may also suggest that action be taken. In general, a consistent temporal or demographic pattern of individual exposures within the IRR should elicit greater attention than a random pattern. For example several individual workers in a cardiac catheterization laboratory may consistently receive exposures just below the upper bound of the IRR while the other workers receive a variety of exposures. The institution may decide to initiate optimization activities for these workers even though none of them exceeded the IRR.

Action levels based on individual exposures do not address the problem of collective dose. From a societal point of view, collective dose is as important as individual dose because total radiation detriment is assumed to be proportional to collective dose. Because of the critical dependence of collective dose on workload, staff patterns, work patterns, and complexity of procedures, it is difficult to set numerical collective dose guidelines. The practice and experience of similar institutions may be useful in setting initial goals. It is possible for an institution to monitor its collective dose over a period of time, as shown in Figure 4.2. Once suffcent data are available, the standard deviation of the collective dose can be calculated. A Collective Reference Range (CRR) should then be identifiable based upon the precision and trend of the data. The lower and upper bounds of the CRR may be set approximately one and two standard deviations (respectively) above the mean collective dose equivalent, although institutional experience and discretion should be used to determine their precise value. The Collective Reference Range is

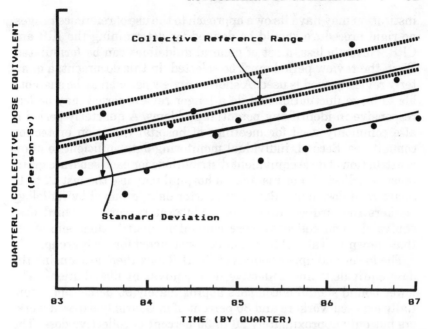

Fig. 4.2 Representative plot of collective dose versus time. The variability and trend of the data have been used to determine the Collective Reference Region. See text for explanation.

defined to be that range of collective dose equivalent values that, if exceeded, automatically triggers optimization activity. If the CRR is not exceeded, it is presumed that "collective" radiation protection is optimal and no action need be taken. (However, action may still be needed based on individual doses.) A collective dose that falls within the CRR may or may not stimulate optimization activity, based upon institutional discretion.

For larger institutions, it is preferable to monitor the collective dose of identifiable subgroups separately, (e.g., diagnostic imaging personnel, radiation oncology personnel), in order to reduce the chance of offsetting trends. If possible, workload data should be obtained for the period over which the collective dose is analyzed because workload fluctuations often are the greatest source of fluctuation in collective dose.

4.4 Summary of Guidelines for Determining the IRR and CRR

Because the dose equivalent characteristics of institutions and subgroups within institutions are not identical, and because each institution may have its own approach to the use of reference ranges, no rigid procedure should be defined for determining the IRR and CRR. Nevertheless, a set of general guidelines can be formulated. First, the review period must be selected. In this document, a quarterly review period is used. A shorter review period may be susceptible to large fluctuations while a longer review period may be less responsive in identifying potential problems. A quarterly period is also commonly used for meetings of hospital radiation protection committees. Second, individual monitoring data sufficient to allow construction of dose equivalent distributions for each separate group must be collected. For instance, a hospital may use the last 12 to 16 quarters of dose equivalent per quarter data, grouped by radiology workers and cardiac catheterization laboratory workers. Third, dose equivalent and collective dose equivalent distributions similar to that shown in Table 3.2 should be constructed for each group.

The lower and upper bounds of the IRR may then be set using the dose equivalent and collective dose equivalent distributions. The lower bound should encompass approximately 90 percent of potentially exposed workers and 80 percent of measurably exposed workers but only approximately 20 to 30 percent of collective dose. The upper bound of the IRR should be set to encompass approximately 99 percent of potentially exposed workers and approximately 95 percent of measurably exposed workers. In many cases the lower bound of the IRR will be approximately equal to the mean dose equivalent of measurably exposed workers while the upper bound will be 3 to 5 times that value. This approximation may be useful for cases in which there are insufficient data to construct meaningful dose equivalent distributions.

Finally, collective dose equivalent per review period should be analyzed by group for trends and variance. The lower bound of the CRR should be approximately equal to the mean collective dose per review period plus one standard deviation, while the upper bound should be approximately equal to the mean plus two standard deviations.

5. A Practical Approach to Implementation of ALARA

5.1 Rationale

The process of assuring that radiation exposures are ALARA may be viewed as an ongoing series of decisions about possible radiation protection actions. However, decision criteria for implementing ALARA cannot be formulated in the same manner as dose limitations that employ simple numerical thresholds and imperative rules. In some cases, a mathematical process can be formulated with an outcome that may be used as a numerical decision threshold. In the majority of cases encountered in the medical environment, however, the decision process is largely qualitative and intuitive, with a substantial component of non-quantifiable value judgement. A practical approach to implementation of ALARA in a medical setting must, therefore, provide a framework for the decision-making process without explicitly determining the outcome of any individual decision.

5.2 Description of Approach

The approach to implementing ALARA discussed in this report addresses only the operation of a program within the context of a pre-existing and properly functioning medical radiation protection program. Although the principle of ALARA and the criteria for "standard" radiation protection are not entirely separable, it is not the purpose of this report to review all aspects of medical radiation protection.

The framework for a medically oriented ALARA program is diagrammed in the flow chart in Figure 5.1. The major components of the system, discussed in detail below, are as follows: identification of potential problems for consideration, assessment of a particular potential problem, identification of possible responses, acquisition of optimization information for each possible response, application of

33

the decision process, implementation of optimal response, and assessment of results. The flow chart does not include an "end" statement because this process is ongoing. **The intent of this approach is to give guidance on how an individual institution might develop its own method rather than to impose a particular method on the medical radiation safety program.** Adaptation to local operations, cost, capabilities and social factors is the essence of implementing ALARA.

5.2.1 *Identification of Potential Problems for Consideration*

The initial step in the ongoing implementation process is the identification of potential problems most deserving of assessment. Since the only result of this step is further assessment, unrefined data and informal procedures may be used. The most important quantitative technique is periodic review of personnel monitoring records. A flow chart for a review system based on an Individual Reference Range (IRR) and a Collective Reference Range (CRR) is shown in Figure 5.1. First, each individual exposure is compared to the IRR. As discussed previously, many individual exposures are expected to be less than the IRR, and only a few percent of individual exposures are expected to exceed the IRR. For those individuals having exposures less than the IRR, no further action is required. Individuals with exposures exceeding the IRR are referred automatically to the "further assessment" stage of the optimization process. Individual doses within the IRR may be reviewed further to decide whether action is justified (see discussion in Section 4.3). After individual records are reviewed it is necessary to review collective dose records. The collective dose and collective reference range are calculated from current and past collective dose records as previously described. In institutions in which large subgroups have significantly dissimilar occupational exposure patterns, it may be desirable to consider each subgroup separately. If the collective dose for a group or subgroup exceeds the CRR, then that group is referred to the "further assessment" stage of optimization. Of course, the fact that an IRR or CRR has been exceeded does not necessarily indicate that a non-optimal situation exists. That determination is made only when a response other than "take no action" results from the subsequent optimization considerations. If all individual exposures are less than the individual reference range, and if the collective dose is less than the collective reference range, then no further optimization action is required on the basis of personnel monitoring records.

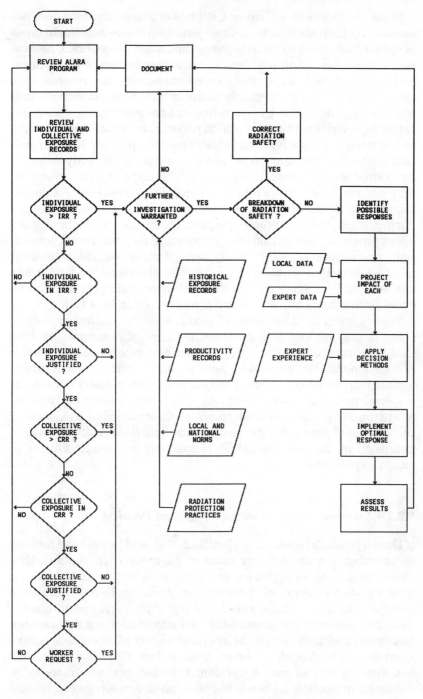

Fig. 5.1 Flow chart for implementation of an ALARA program.

Since the fact that an IRR or CRR has not been exceeded does not necessarily indicate that an optimal situation exists, additional types of data may be used to initiate the optimization procedure. Observation of procedures and practices by various members of the medical and technical staff can be used to supplement exposure records. This type of input can be particularly useful in identifying situations that might escape detection by individual or area monitoring. Examples range from circumstances in which personal monitors are not worn, or are worn improperly, to circumstances that produce highly localized exposures that may be missed by a single whole body monitor. Individual workers may also question whether radiation protection for a particular procedure is being appropriately observed. Examples might include inquiries from ward nurses about their exposures during brachytherapy procedures, and questions from technologists about proximity to a patient during an imaging procedure. Observations and requests are inherently non-quantitative, and judgement must be exercised when deciding to refer the situation for further assessment. Past experience of the institution and published experiences from other institutions are primary aids in this task.

Finally, even in the absence of quantitative or qualitative indications, it may be known from the experience of recognized experts that certain problems are likely to arise and hence, may be worthy of assessment. For example, there is ample evidence that wraparound lead aprons can reduce body exposures of persons working in a special procedures laboratory. An institution not currently using wraparound aprons may wish to assess their potential use, even in the absence of problematic exposure data. This document and reports published in the professional literature may be used as sources of expert experience.

5.2.2 *Assessment of a Particular Potential Problem*

Once a potential problem is identified, it should be assessed further in accordance with the flow chart of Figure 5.1. In general, this assessment involves gathering more extensive information than was used for identification of the potential problem. Exposure records pertinent to the problem should be critically reviewed to ensure that they accurately represent the real situation. Personal monitor placement and applicability of interpretation of effective dose equivalent should be considered by each institution. (Monitor placement and applicability of dose equivalent recorded has been more fully discussed in Section 2.) Since higher exposure readings can be due to changes in workload, data should be obtained about the complexity and number of procedures, as well as the number of personnel involved. Individual and collective dose data corrected for inaccuracy and representativeness should then be recompared with the IRR and CRR of the group or subgroup being reviewed to be sure that the indication of a potential problem is still valid. In addition, the collective dose per unit workload should be compared with representative local and national values to ascertain whether an observed increase in collective dose is due to an increase of workload or the complexity of workload rather than to non-optimal radiation protection. Non-quantitative observations can be compared with past observations of normal practice or similar published accounts. If the quantitative or qualitative descriptors of the potential problem exceed these normative values, then sufficient evidence exists to warrant further investigation.

Potential problems with characteristics that do not exceed normal values do not necessarily represent optimal procedures. When feasible, these apparently normal situations should be examined to see whether further improvements are possible. However, it should be recognized that some areas have more potential for improvement than others and the cost of detailed consideration of a problem may exceed the potential cost reductions associated with detriment reduction.

Some potential problems may be caused by a breakdown in standard radiation safety practice. For instance, an individual may be neglecting to use lead gloves for palpation during fluoroscopy. This would obviously result in elevated finger badge readings, but is not a problem that requires optimization procedures for its solution. Of course any problem of this type must be corrected and documented.

5.2.3 *Identification of Possible Responses*

After a potential problem has been identified, it is then necessary to identify all possible responses using both local experience and expert experience, as found in this report and in the professional literature. As shown in the flow chart of Figure 5.2, five general classifications of possible response can be identified: take no action, modify shielding, modify procedures, modify equipment and modify personnel system and/or training. "Take no action" must always be considered since this represents the appropriate response to any situation that is ultimately shown to be optimal. "Modify shielding" denotes actions such as adding structural shielding, acquiring portable shields or wraparound lead aprons. "Modify procedure" denotes possible changes in the manner in which a procedure is performed

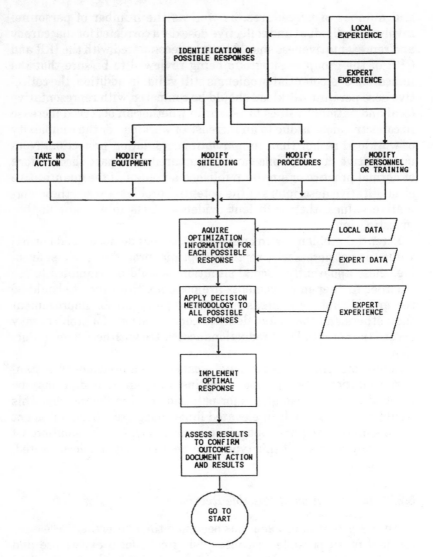

Fig. 5.2 Detail of a portion of Figure 5.1 showing decision tree for identification of possible responses to a potential problem.

such that less time is spent in radiation areas, greater distance is interposed between radiation sources and personnel or less radiation is required to complete the procedure. "Modify equipment" denotes improvements in existing equipment or purchase of new equipment which may result in lower occupational exposure. Examples are equipment with improved image receptor sensitivity or improved design that reduces leakage or scatter radiation. As will be discussed in Section 5.2.4, special consideration must be given to any equipment change that impacts upon patient care. "Modify personnel system and/or training" denotes possible changes in the number, duties or requisite competency of personnel, as well as in-service training activities to increase the radiation protection awareness of personnel and to motivate personnel to use good radiation protection practices. The better the cause of a situation is understood, the more reasonable will be the response. For instance, increasing the shielding of an angiographic control booth will not reduce exposures to personnel who are unable to leave the patient's side during a procedure. In many cases it may be useful to consider a possible response that is a combination of the several categories discussed here.

5.2.4 *Acquisition of Optimization Information for Each Possible Response*

After identification of each possible response it is necessary to acquire data on both the expected cost of implementation and the expected effect of the response on exposure patterns. Cost of implementation should include all capital and operational costs. For possible responses with far reaching consequences, it is also advisable to review the cost experience of other institutions undertaking similar projects. If a proposed response can affect patient care (*i.e.*, a change in image receptor that results in a change in image quality), it is necessary to demonstrate either that the benefit to the patient is not decreased or, if it is evident that the benefit will be decreased, to assign a monetary cost to the change. Not only is this latter task extremely difficult, but it also implies that immediate benefits to individual patients can be compared to long-term stochastic benefits to a group of occupationally exposed workers. For these reasons it may be desirable, whenever possible, to consider alternatives that have either beneficial or minimal adverse impact on patient care. In cases in which a proposed change may impact patient care, the proposed change must be thoroughly discussed and agreed upon by the medical staff prior to implementation.

Estimating the effect on exposure patterns is often more difficult than estimating the cost of implementation. Changes in exposure patterns can be estimated with a reasonably precise knowledge of the relative contributions of various sources of exposure, their relation to radiation protection operational guidelines and the degree to which these guidelines are actually observed by the workers. If a quantitative estimate of the anticipated change in collective dose can be made, it may then be converted to monetary terms using an agreed upon value of α, which has units of $/person-Sv. In many cases, this type of analysis will either be impossible or will have such a high degree of uncertainty that it is of little value. It then becomes necessary to rely primarily on qualitative judgement and the experience of similar institutions to assess the potential impact. Various possible responses may be coarsely ranked as being expected to have little, moderate, or large anticipated effect on individual and collective dose.

5.2.5 *Application of the Decision Process to All Possible Responses*

At this point there is sufficient information to make a decision about which of the several possible responses is optimal. In the small number of cases that can be reliably cast in purely monetary terms, the decision consists simply of choosing the option that minimizes the total cost of protection plus detriment. Another comparatively simple choice occurs when one of the possible options provides a favorable effect on individual or collective dose for little or no cost. For example, informing technologists of the best place to stand during fluroscopic procedures, or giving a lecture on safe handling of isotopes, costs very little but can yield desirable results. In some cases, an institution may wish to implement trivial cost options first regardless of expected dose reduction, monitor the results, and then consider more costly options later if the desired result is not achieved. While this approach may not be optimization in its ideal sense, it does recognize the uncertainties involved in decision analysis and the desire to conserve resources.

Inevitably, cases will arise in which no zero cost options, other than "take no action", are available and in which accurate formal cost-benefit analyses are impossible. These cases often involve options of known costs that represent a significant expense, and benefits that are uncertain or only coarsely known. The lack of easy options and the uncertainty in the data required to make a decision necessitate significant reliance on intuition and value judgement. Qualitative considerations, such as the institutional philosophy towards radiation protection and the potential effect of the decision on the public image of the institution, may influence the choice of options. Guidance may be available from reports from other institutions that have faced similar problems, and from the consultation of a qualified expert having appropriate experience in the particular radiation protection problem.

5.2.6 *Implementation of Optimal Response, Assessment of Results and Documentation*

The optimal response should be implemented in a timely fashion. Changes in operational procedures are often difficult to implement, because they depend more upon the diligence and competence of the staff than on physical changes. Therefore, it may be advisable to monitor the activities of staff as well as their exposure patterns. Before a measure is deemed a failure it is well to confirm that it was really tried. Small improvements may take some time to detect, and may be easily masked by statistical fluctuations. If a response does fail, it is advisable to analyze the reason for failure before trying the next option, since failure of a particular option may be indicative of faulty analysis of the underlying causes of the problem.

Each time the radiation protection program is reviewed for compliance with the ALARA requirement, the review should be documented. Such documentation should include the reference ranges used to review monitoring records, the nature of incidents triggering further investigations, the results of those investigations, a summary of responses considered, justification for the chosen response and the results of the implementation of that response.

6. Implementation of ALARA in Diagnostic X-ray Imaging

6.1 Sources of Occupational Exposure in X-ray Imaging

This section deals with sources of occupational exposure associated with diagnostic x-ray imaging. Dental radiography is covered separately in Section 9. Table 6.1 shows a scheme for the classification of procedures leading to potential exposure.

Occupational radiation exposure in medicine depends upon a number of factors, the most important of which is the x-ray procedure. There are three general procedures that constitute sources of exposure: radiography, fluoroscopy and special examinations. Radiography is by far the most widely used x-ray imaging modality and is the most significant contributor to the medical radiation exposure of the general population. Fluoroscopic procedures on the other hand, including those of a special nature, constitute fewer than 10 percent of all examinations (NCRP, 1989b), but are the largest source of occupational radiation exposure by far.

Examples of unnecessary occupational exposure abound in each of these areas. Efforts to optimize radiation protection may be neces-

TABLE 6.1—*Procedures having the potential for radiation exposure in diagnostic x-ray imaging*

Radiography	Fluoroscopy	Special examinations
General purpose	General purpose	Cardiac catheterization
hospital	hospital	Angiography
private office	private office	neurologic
Special purpose	Mobile C-arm	abdominal
trauma		digital subtraction
orthopedic		Interventional procedures
cystographic		angioplasty
chiropractic		embolization
Mobile		
Tomography		
Computed tomography		
Mammography		

sary in all three. However, the appropriate approach will differ by type of x-ray procedure. Once the x-ray procedure has been identified, additional factors may become apparent. Location, size and type of facility, complexity of procedures, workload, ancillary imaging apparatus and protective barrier design are additional factors that will influence the approach to ALARA at a particular facility.[1]

Workload is one factor, whether expressed in the classical terms of mA-min/wk (see NCRP Report No. 49, NCRP, 1976) or simply the number of radiographic exposures or the time that the fluoroscopic beam is energized. In general, occupational exposures will be directly proportional to any of these measures of workload. Workload is a more important consideration during fluoroscopy, special and interventional procedures, because usually imaging physicians and technologists are both present in the examination room during beam-on time. Lack of appropriate training by medical and technical staff can also lead to higher workload, resulting in increased patient exposure and occupational exposure.

6.1.1 Radiography

Approximately 90 percent of diagnostic x-ray examinations are radiographic in nature (NCRP, 1989b). Most are conducted in hospitals with general purpose, overhead radiographic tubes. Approximately 30 percent of such exposures, however, are conducted outside of hospitals, and that percentage appears to be increasing (NCRP, 1989b). The growth in numbers of stand-alone imaging centers, emergency clinics and medical clinics is rapidly changing the mix of hospital and non-hospital x-ray examinations.

The complement of radiographic equipment found in a hospital will depend considerably on the size and the nature of that hospital. Small community hospitals will usually contain one to four examination rooms, half of which will be radiographic only and the remainder, radiographic-fluoroscopic. Approximately 70 percent of U.S. hospitals have fewer than 200 beds and would thus be considered small community hospitals (AHA, 1984). In such a hospital, the number of staff technologists and imaging physicians will be small and the principal source of occupational radiation exposure will be fluoroscopy.

---

[1]In several locations in this section, occupational exposures are listed for specific x-ray imaging procedures. In some cases these exposures reflect the experience of one or a few institutions and may not represent average exposures nationally or exposures consistent with ALARA levels.

During radiography the technologist will stand in a control booth that is typically shielded as a secondary barrier against x-ray tube head leakage and scattered radiation from the patient. Depending on room size and barrier thickness, the dose equivalent to a technologist in the control booth area is typically less than 1 μSv for a single film taken with a technique of 80 kVp and 40 mAs.

Small community hospitals will also usually have one or two mobile radiographic units that will be used not only in patient rooms, but also in surgery and in the emergency room. The number of mobile units increases as the hospital size increases; rule of thumb suggests at least one mobile unit for every 100 beds. Since mobile units operate in unshielded environments they are often a cause for concern. Studies of scattered radiation from mobile units indicate that air kerma at a distance of one meter from the patient may range from 0.4 to 1 μGy per film for a technique of 80 kVp and 4 mAs (North, 1985; Herman et al., 1980). Since mobile radiographic equipment is operated in unshielded environments, and since it may not produce an image quality equivalent to that of fixed equipment, it is desirable that, whenever possible, the radiographs should be produced in the radiology department using permanently installed equipment. Mobile radiographic equipment should not be operated by non-radiology personnel.

As hospital size increases, radiographic equipment becomes more numerous and perhaps more specialized. A large general hospital will have a complement of specialty radiographic equipment. One or more rooms may be devoted to conventional tomography. Occupational exposure per procedure during a tomographic examination may be higher than in other radiographic examinations if a large number of views is obtained.

Computed tomography (CT) is essential to any large hospital and is frequently found in small hospitals. Although patient exposures may be high in CT, personnel exposure levels are usually low, because the primary x-ray beam is highly collimated and scattered radiation levels are low. In all such scanners, leakage radiation has been reduced to near zero. For personnel who are located in the control room of a properly designed facility, computed tomography does not represent a significant source of occupational exposure. Only if an individual is required to remain in the room with the patient during the examination can a measurable exposure be expected. Depending on technique factors, air kerma levels of 5 to 20 μGy per slice have been measured near the gantry opening (Jacobson and Kelly, 1986; Kaczmarek et al., 1986). Higher exposure levels are associated with the use of high resolution CT which involves thin slices at high x-ray intensities.

In the past, mammography was done in many hospitals, regardless of size, with a conventional overhead radiographic tube. However, recent standards for mammographic imaging have emphasized the importance of dedicated equipment and specialized technique (NCRP, 1986). Screen-film mammography should not be performed unless a molybdenum target x-ray tube is used (NCRP, 1986). Such tubes are now available, but only when incorporated into dedicated equipment. With dedicated equipment, occupational exposures in mammography are indistinguishable from background, if appropriate radiation protection is used. The x-ray beam energy is low, 50 kVp or less, and the primary beam is, by design, limited to the size of the image receptor. The image receptor holder, in turn, is backed by lead. Consequently, the technologist is exposed only to secondary radiation which is easily controlled by a window-wall type barrier equivalent to approximately 0.2 mm Pb.

Other specialty radiographic equipment may be found in the hospital. Orthopedic surgery may have a dedicated trauma room. The emergency service may have one or more rooms equipped with an overhead radiographic unit. Urology may be provided with a cystographic unit. Each of these x-ray sources can contribute significantly to occupational exposure if radiation control procedures are not adequate.

Radiographic equipment may also be located in private offices. The term private office as used in this document relates to several different settings. In addition to the classical private physician office, there are stand-alone imaging centers, free-standing medical clinics and free-standing emergency clinics. In a recent year, approximately 9 percent of medical diagnostic x-ray examinations were conducted in radiologists offices, 4 percent in other physicians offices, 3 percent in podiatrists offices and 5.5 percent in chiropractors offices (NCRP, 1989b). Occupational exposure from private office-based radiographic procedures should be similar to that in hospitals, if appropriate radiation protection measures are observed and the staff has appropriate training in the operation of radiographic equipment. Workloads are often light in private offices. In such cases, radiographic-only private-office based personnel monitoring results may reveal only minimum detectable values.

6.1.2 Fluoroscopy

The use of fluoroscopy for diagnostic imaging represents the largest source of occupational exposure in medicine. During fluoroscopy, the x-ray tube may be energized for considerable periods of time. Fluoroscopic procedures require that the operator be present in the examination room and, when present, usually in close proximity to the radiation source and the patient. In fact, the patient becomes the most intense source of occupational exposure because of scattered radiation. Without protective drapery, air kerma rates near the patient may exceed 2 mGy h^{-1}, depending on fluoroscopic technique factors. The use of remote-control fluoroscopic equipment allows the radiologist to perform examinations with essentially no occupational exposure. However, if remote fluoroscopic procedures require personnel to remain in the room while the beam is energized, air kerma levels even higher than those of conventional fluoroscopy may result, due to the overhead tube geometry and the absence of protective drapes.

A source of occupational exposure of frequent concern is the mobile C-arm fluoroscope. This device is used principally in surgery but may also be used at the patient's bedside. During its use, physicians and operators are present in close proximity to the patient. Radiographic views, as well as fluoroscopic exposures, are involved. *All personnel present during the procedure must wear protective aprons.* Unlike conventional fluoroscopic procedures, it is often impossible to use protective drapes to shield personnel from scattered radiation. Air kerma rates at the location of operating personnel have been reported to range from 0.5 to 2 mGy h^{-1} at a distance of approximately 50 cm from the patient using a technique of 110 kVp, 2.5 mA for orthopedic procedures (Miller *et al.*, 1983). Exposure levels depend upon the location of the x-ray tube. Geometries with the x-ray tube over the table may increase personnel exposure by a factor of approximately three. Hence, the x-ray tube should be located under the patient as often as possible. Adding to the potential hazard of such a device is the manner in which the primary beam can be pointed in nearly any direction. The potential for exposure of personnel to the primary beam is greater here than with any other procedure. C-arm fluoroscopy examinations are normally performed by physicians other than radiologists. Consequently, it is essential that a trained radiologic technologist either operate the unit or have trained others to be responsible for them to do so.

6.1.3 *Special Examinations*

The term "special procedures" as employed in radiology generally refers to angiography and its application in neuroradiology and vascular radiology. The term "special examinations" is employed here to identify not only special procedures, but also some additional imaging procedures such as cardiac catheterization that constitute a potential source of high occupational exposures. Diagnostic ultra-sound, thermography and magnetic resonance imaging are not considered, because they do not contribute to patient or occupational ionizing radiation exposure.

In addition to a general purpose fluoroscopic system that might be present in either a hospital or a private office, fixed fluoroscopic systems for dedicated use exist. One or more angiography suites to support neurologic and other vascular needs may be present in most general hospitals. Fluoroscopic times are long, and accompanying radiographic exposures can be numerous. Imaging physicians and technologists are nearly always present in the room and close to the patient during such examinations.

It is often difficult to shield against scattered radiation, and, even when able to be used, the shield may not benefit all of the staff present. Staff exposure rates associated with the examinations in such rooms can be 2 mGy h^{-1}, or more, depending on location and fluoroscopic technique.

For some procedures, digital subtraction angiography (DSA) may be used instead of conventional special examinations that employ a film-screen image receptor. Even though an image intensifier is the image receptor utilized for DSA, the exposure per image may be as high as that of a film-screen image receptor. Hence, occupational exposures associated with DSA examinations are similar to those of conventional special examinations.

Cardiac catheterization can result in elevated personnel monitoring results. Like other vascular procedures, fluoroscopic times are long, personnel are in close proximity to the patient, and scatter shielding is difficult. Air kerma rates to personnel during fluoroscopy are in the range of 0.5 to 2 mGy h^{-1}. For gantry-mounted fluoroscopic systems, *e.g.*, C-, U- and LU-arm gantry configurations, the air kerma rates vary greatly with gantry orientation. Procedures implemented in the cardiac catheterization laboratory involve not only radiography and fluoroscopy, but also require cineradiography. Cineradiography can result in exceptionally high patient doses with associated elevated occupational exposures. During cineradiography, the table-top air kerma rate may vary from 0.2 to 1 Gy min^{-1}. Although a patient examination may require only 30 to 40 seconds of cineradiographic time, total exposures are still high.

6.2 Normative Patterns of Occupational Exposure and Workload, and Indicators for Suspicion of Non-ALARA Situations

In the previous section, more than a dozen specific sources of occupational exposure in diagnostic x-ray imaging were identified. To assess occupational exposures and their trends for the purpose of maintaining exposures ALARA, it is not convenient to consider these sources separately. Rather, it is more appropriate to consider occupational exposures according to the employment situation of the individual or group. Many radiology personnel work with multiple procedures involving exposure to x rays. Therefore, when a situation arises, which may be considered to be non-ALARA, some guidance is appropriate as to which of the procedures should be evaluated first.

Many radiologic technologists and imaging physicians will function in what might be called either radiographic-only or general radiology activities. These two occupational classifications would hold regardless of the place of employment. In general radiology, the individual would very likely come into contact with radiography, fluoroscopy and special examinations. (Although as discussed below, special examinations may be performed only by a relatively small subgroup of individuals.) Radiographic-only personnel would be those assigned to x-ray examination rooms in hospitals and in private offices housing only radiographic facilities. These two occupational categories compose the bulk of exposed radiologic personnel.

In addition to these two principal occupational groups, the radiation safety officer (RSO) may be faced with situations involving other select and identifiably separate groups. Those involved in computed tomography and mammography (subgroups of radiographic-only personnel) would be expected to receive little, if any, radiation exposure. However, persons whose principal assignments are in angiography, C-arm fluoroscopy or cardiac catheterization, could experience a considerably higher than average occupational exposure. Each of these occupationally exposed groups will be considered separately in detail.

6.2.1 General Radiology

The typical radiologic technologist employed in general radiology would spend most of the time in the radiographic and radiographic-fluoroscopic examination rooms. The workload might consist of a larger amount of radiographic exposures (particularly chest radiography) and a lesser amount of fluoroscopic studies. However, on occasion, if not frequently, that individual might be required to assist in any of the other areas in diagnostic radiology. In general, most of the reported dose equivalent will be the result of fluoroscopic activity, whether it be in general fluoroscopy or other procedures requiring fluoroscopy. The NCRP and EPA have reported the occupational exposure characteristics for hospital based personnel (NCRP, 1989a; EPA, 1984).

Since the majority of this group is involved in general radiology, these figures may be useful in approximating the characteristics of personnel exposure patterns. In 1980, the mean annual dose equivalent to all hospital based personnel (employees in all job categories potentially exposed to radiation) was 1.4 mSv. Measurably exposed hospital based personnel are a subgroup defined as those monitored employees in all job categories receiving at least 0.1 mSv/y. The mean annual dose equivalent for this subgroup was 2 mSv. Ninety-five percent of hospital-based personnel received less than 7.5 mSv/y. Hospital based personnel received a collective dose of 172 person-Sv from all sources in 1980. Johnson and Abernathy (1983) estimated that there were 151 million hospital-based radiographic, fluoroscopic and special examinations in 1980. This implies that the average collective dose equivalent per procedure in 1980 was approximately 1.1 person-μSv/procedure. If it is assumed that fluoroscopic and special examinations, which constitute only 10 percent of total examinations, account for 90 percent of collective dose, then the average collective dose per fluoroscopic or special procedure is approximately 10 person-μSv/procedure while the average collective dose per radiographic-only procedure is approximately 0.1 person-μSv/procedure.[2]

To illustrate the use of normative patterns in setting reference ranges, consider the following hypothetical example. The radiology department of a 300-bed community hospital contains seven imaging rooms including chest radiography, general radiography, radiography-fluoroscopy, special procedures and CT. The department performs 40,000 procedures per year, including 4,000 fluoroscopic and special procedures, with a staff of 35 monitored personnel. Technologists are rotated every three months through all areas. A review of monitoring records indicates that 23 personnel received some dose; that the average annual dose equivalent of measurably exposed workers is about 1.9 mSv and that 95 percent of measurably exposed personnel receive less than 8 mSv. A review of quarterly records reveals an average dose equivalent for measurably exposed workers of approximately 0.5 mSv with 95 percent of personnel receiving less

[2]These figures were derived as follows: Fluoroscopic and special procedures account for 10 percent (15 million) of the 151 million hospital-based procedures and are assumed to result in 90 percent (155 person-Sv) of the 172 person-Sv hospital-based collective dose, yielding an average collective dose per procedure of 10.3 person-μSv/procedure. Similarly, the 90 percent (136 million) radiographic-only procedures were assumed to account for 10 percent (17 person-Sv) of hospital-based collective dose, yielding an average collective dose per procedure of 0.125 person-μSv/procedure. The figures were then rounded to 0.1 μSv per procedure.

than 2.5 mSv. The quarterly records show a greater variability of dose equivalent, due to the manner in which personnel are rotated through the various duties. The collective dose per quarter is approximately 11 ± 2 person-mSv. Following the procedures outlined in Section 4.3, a reasonable choice of reference ranges would be an IRR of 0.5 to 2.5 mSv/qtr and a CRR of 13 to 15 person-mSv/qtr. Other institutions, facing different individual situations, would establish different reference ranges.

6.2.2 *Radiographic Only (Including Mammography)*

Personnel involved only in radiographic exposures are usually employed in private offices, medical clinics and emergency clinics. Less often, hospital based personnel may be permanently assigned to a radiographic room. In either case, the absence of fluoroscopic sources of radiation results in lower occupational exposures. The EPA reported a mean annual dose to potentially exposed private practice personnel of 1 mSv and a mean annual dose to exposed private practice personnel of 1.8 mSv (EPA, 1984). However, this group also included private practice fluoroscopic exposure. Accurate workload data for private practice radiographic facilities are not readily available. However, the data of hospital based radiographic examinations may be representative. Hence, as discussed in Section 6.2.1, a collective dose per radiographic procedure of approximately 0.1 person-μSv might be expected.

A small, private practice, radiographic-only facility is likely to encounter little measurable exposure if proper radiation protection practices are observed. If a higher than normal occupational exposure is encountered, a higher than normal workload may be the cause. Few radiographic rooms located outside of a hospital will experience a workload in excess of 200 mA-min/wk. Most will show less than 100 mA-min/wk. This is understandable since in many such facilities, most of the exposures are of extremities or chest. These types of examinations require very low air kerma rates.

For those involved exclusively with mammography, such as at the many breast cancer detection centers, the vendor of the personnel radiation monitoring device should be informed that only low energy x-radiation is involved. This will allow more accurate analysis of the personnel monitor.

Workloads in mammography can be high if the equipment is fully utilized. A normal study involving two views of each breast, a cranio-caudad and a medio-lateral, will require approximately 100 mAs for screen-film mammography and 300 mAs for xeromammography.

Only breast imaging centers would be expected to experience a full patient load. Regardless of the workload, occupational exposures are usually nil because of the low energy x-ray beam and the incorporation of effective shielding against scattered radiation as an integral part of dedicated mammographic imaging equipment. The imaging physician or technologist should always stand behind this shielding rather than beside the patient. Under these circumstances, the operator will rarely receive a measurable radiation exposure.

Facilities having a monitoring record showing other than minimum detectable readings may determine action levels in a manner analogous to that discussed under General Radiology. For facilities with a history of minimum detectable monitor results, the individual reference range is from minimum detectable which is often 100 µSv to perhaps 500 µSv/qtr.

6.2.3 Computed Tomography

Many institutions have specific CT personnel who, due to their specialized training, do not perform general radiologic duties. In such circumstances, it may be necessary to consider them separately in optimization programs. Workloads associated with CT are very high. Depending upon the type of scanner, the number of patients examined and the number of images obtained per examination, workloads can range from 5,000 to 20,000 mA-min/wk. A busy CT facility will examine three patients per hour and average 15 to 25 images per patient.

In spite of the heavy workload, personnel exposures in CT are usually minimal. It is unusual for any personnel in a CT facility to receive a measurable exposure. Only if an individual is required to remain in the room during an examination is it likely that an exposure will be registered. Then, of course, the individual will be provided with protective apparel. In one report (Jacobson and Kelly, 1986), a maximum dose equivalent outside of protective apparel of 0.4 mSv/procedure occurred during contrast injection for a whole body CT procedure. Institutions that conduct most of the CT procedures from the control room would set reference ranges similar to those of radiographic-only facilities. If frequent in-room procedures are required, CT exposure patterns would approach those of fluoroscopic facilities, and reference ranges would be set accordingly.

6.2.4 Angiography and Special Procedures

Angiographic procedures provide enhanced visualization of vessels by injection of radiopaque contrast material during image acquisition. In addition to the standard procedures of neuroangiography and vascular angiography, many interventional procedures such as angioplasty and embolization have been developed in recent years. All of these procedures involve considerable fluoroscopy time and multiple radiographic images. Consequently, the radiation environment may include high air kerma levels.

The workload in angiography is usually low unless it is a specialty facility. Normally, not more than six or eight cases can be done per day in an angiography room. In many hospitals, the case load will not exceed two or three per day. In a busy angiography room, weekly workloads of 1,000 mA-min and 500 mA-min for fluoroscopy and radiography, respectively, will be exceeded only rarely. Still, personnel exposures can be high. Riley *et al.* (1972) reported mean exposures to various areas of the body during angiography, myelography and bronchography. Readings at the forehead and collar ranged from 60 to 270 μSv per procedure with the highest readings for abdominal angiography and the lowest readings for cerebral angiography. In this study, approximately 90 percent of the exposure was received during the injection of the contrast media. Lower values may be expected if remote power injection is used. Santen *et al.* (1975) reported forehead exposures per procedure averaging from 7 to 150 μSv for various special procedures and that 90 percent or more of the personnel exposure was attributable to rapid film changer (serial radiography) exposures during and immediately after manual injection.

Gustafsson and Lunderquist (1981) estimated annual dose equivalents to imaging physicians performing some types of angiographic procedures at their institution. For an imaging physician performing 25 percutaneous transhepatic portographies plus 25 percutaneous transhepatic cholangiographies, an average and maximum annual dose equivalent of 4.3 and 13 mSv were estimated. The average collective dose per procedure was 0.09 person-mSv. Brateman *et al.* (1979) reported individual and collective dose equivalents from a suite performing various types of angiographies. Before installation of a transparent protective barrier, monitor reports averaged 10.75 mSv/qtr and the collective dose per procedure averaged 0.27 person-mSv. After the scatter shielding was added, monitor reports averaged 3.58 mSv/qtr and the collective dose per procedure was 0.1 person-mSv.

National data are not available for comparison since the EPA could not determine job specialization from film-badge records. However, the value of 10 person-μSv/procedure indirectly derived from EPA data (Section 6.2.1) for all types of fluoroscopic procedures is at the lower end of the anecdotal data summarized above.

Small institutions typically will not assign personnel to only angiography/special procedures. Reference ranges for the institutions would be developed as part of the general radiology ALARA program. Larger institutions may have the workload and staffing patterns to justify separate action levels for individuals assigned to these procedures. As a hypothetical example, a large hospital may have two rooms dedicated to angiography/special procedures; one a gantry-mounted polydirectional imaging system and the other a conventional tube-under fluoroscopic system. The total staff for both rooms might be four radiologic technologists, two imaging physicians and one nurse. If the two rooms perform an average of 1,500 procedures per year, the average annual dose equivalent might be expected to range from 15 to 20 mSv, and a quarterly reference range of 4.5 to 13 mSv/qtr may be expected. All of these values refer to a film badge worn outside protective apparel in the region of the collar and should not be interpreted to be the actual effective whole body dose equivalent received by personnel.

6.2.5 *Mobile C-Arm Fluoroscopy*

Many operative procedures require the assistance of a mobile C-arm fluoroscopic unit. Fracture reduction, prosthesis placement, hip pinning, and implantation of temporary pacemakers are a few of the more frequent applications of the mobile C-arm fluoroscope. Air kerma rates around a mobile C-arm fluoroscope may be somewhat lower than those around a conventional fluoroscope, because smaller fields are employed. However, lack of shielding often negates this advantage. A change in beam orientation greatly alters personnel exposures due to a change in scatter geometry and shielding provided by the patient and operating table. Exposures to operating room personnel are increased when the fluoroscopic beam is directed sideways or down. Lowest occupational exposures are experienced when the beam is directed up. Exposures to both patient and staff can be reduced by use of electronic image storage devices, if beam-on time is reduced because the devices are used.

Reports of dose-equivalent levels associated with various C-arm procedures have appeared in the literature. Miller *et al.* (1983) reported dose equivalent from various orthopedic procedures. Forehead and thyroid dose equivalents ranged from 10 μSv to 1.44 mSv while fluoroscopic beam time ranged from 0.2 to 23 minutes. The forehead and thyroid dose equivalent averaged approximately 50 μSv per minute of fluoroscopic "on" time. Bush *et al.* (1984) and Bush *et al.* (1985) measured dose equivalent levels associated with C-arm assisted renal calculus removal. The average dose equivalent per procedure at the collar level was 100 μSv to the physician, 40 μSv to the surgical nurse, 40 μSv to the radiologic technologist and 30 μSv to the anesthesiologist, for an average fluoroscopy time of 25 minutes. These are anecdotal reports and should not necessarily be considered typical or acceptable at all institutions.

Physicians who employ the C-arm fluoroscope are not usually radiologists and may have little or no training in radiation control. Consequently, it is essential that the C-arm fluoroscope be under the control of someone having adequate training in radiation control such as a registered radiologic technologist. Because high air kerma rates are possible, it is desirable to monitor personnel exposure individually. When personnel are not individually monitored (*i.e.*, an orthopedic surgeon who performs only a few procedures per year at a particular hospital), means should be provided for approximating individual exposure. An effective tool for radiation control is to instruct the technologist to maintain a record of all procedures involving the C-arm fluoroscope. The record should include the following information: date, patient name, physician name, type of study, fluoroscopic beam-on time and number of radiographs. In addition to assuring some recognition of radiation safety by the physician, these data may be helpful in subsequent estimation of patient and unmonitored personnel dose.

Because physicians and technologists may not participate equally in all procedures, separate reference ranges may be appropriate for each. Use of the C-arm fluoroscope may be shared among many physicians, but the same technologist may operate the equipment for all procedures. In departments that do not rotate staff, the technologist assigned to C-arm work may be assigned reference ranges similar to those used in the angiography special procedures grouping since dose equivalent levels and procedure volume may be nearly the same. Institutions may wish to consider separate reference ranges for physicians since, on an individual basis, they may perform fewer procedures than the technologist. However, physicians may receive a higher dose per procedure than technologists due to their closer proximity to the patient.

6.2.6 *Cardiac Catheterization*

This area of radiologic imaging has the potential for producing relatively high occupational exposures. Although the examination room is called the cardiac catheterization laboratory, other procedures, such as pacemaker implantation, percutaneous transluminal coronary angioplasty (PCTA) and patent ductus arteriosis repair with pediatric cases, are conducted there. The use of cinefluorography during cardiac catheterization results in higher personnel exposure. A normal cardiac catheterization will proceed under fluoroscopic control with the patient positioned on the table. A few overhead preliminary radiographs may be necessary. The procedure will conclude with one or more cinefluorographic runs at as much as 0.9 Gy min^{-1}. When multiple views are obtained, the total cinefluorographic run time may be from 30 to 50 seconds. At that level, the air kerma to those attending the patient may be as much as 0.9 mGy min^{-1}, if the rule of thumb applies that the radiation intensity one meter lateral to the patient is 0.1 percent of the entrance beam. It would not take many such procedures to result in a dose equivalent to the operator of several millisieverts.

Personnel exposure during cardiac catheterization procedures has been reported by several authors (Balter *et al.*, 1978; Gustafsson and Lunderquist, 1981; Gertz *et al.*, 1982; Dash and Leaman, 1984; Brahmavar *et al.*, 1984; Jeans *et al.*, 1985). Balter *et al.*, (1978) reported on the results of 700 coronary angiograms utilizing U-arm systems. Nineteen sites were monitored on each operator. The average dose equivalent per study was 0.06 mSv for the eyes and 0.083 mSv for the thyroid when those organs were shielded by special glasses or leaded apparel. In one study Gustafsson and Lunderquist, 1981), it was estimated that a physician performing 120 cardiac angiographies per year would receive approximately 27 mSv to the neck and forehead. Jeans *et al.* (1985) estimated the annual dose equivalent to the eyes of cardiologists performing 250 cardiac catheterizations, 2 angioplasties and 30 pacemaker implants per year to be approximately 43 mSv. However, the recorded dose equivalent of the cardiologist during cineradiography can vary dramatically with location. See Table 6.2 for an appreciation of the effect of distance on the dose equivalent received by staff during cardiac procedures *(e.g.*, cardiologist standing at the side of the x-ray table vs standing at the foot of the table) and of shielding *(e.g.*, with or without lead apron). Dash and Leaman (1984) reported that the dose equivalent to the operator during percutaneous transluminal coronary angioplasty was 93 percent greater than from routine coronary angiography (0.17 mSv/study vs 0.09 mSv/study).

Various studies report the dose equivalent received per cardiac procedure. Values ranged from 0.08 to 0.5 mSv/procedure to the head and eyes, 0.1 to 2 mSv/procedure to the hands and several mSv/procedure at the level of the chest outside of the apron. The dose equivalent per procedure at any particular institution depends greatly on the types of medical procedures and patient characteris-

TABLE 6.2—*Estimated dose equivalent to staff during cardiac studies.[a] After Jeans et al., (1985).*

Category of staff	One catheterization (mSv)				One angioplasty (mSv)				One pacemaker implant (no cine) (mSv)			
	Weighted surface dose No apron	Weighted surface dose With apron	Hands	Eyes	Weighted surface dose No apron	Weighted surface dose With apron	Hands	Eyes	Weighted surface dose No apron	Weighted surface dose With apron	Hands	Eyes
Cardiologist	1.6	0.09	2.1	0.6	3.1	0.2	4.2	1.0	0.14	0.01	0.2	0.05
Cardiologist who stands back during cine	0.3	0.01	0.3	0.2	1.5	0.1	1.9	0.7				
Technologist	0.08	<0.01	0.09	0.02	0.2	0.01	0.2	0.05	0.01	<0.01	0.01	<0.01
Technologist who stands back during cine	0.04	<0.01	0.04	0.01	0.1	0.01	0.1	0.03				
Nurse or anesthetist	0.3	0.02	0.4	0.2	0.8	0.06	0.9	0.5	0.04	<0.01	0.04	0.03

[a]This indicates the type of data that are useful for ALARA determination. In this study the weighted surface dose was estimated by calculating the dose equivalent at the surface of the body over each critical organ. The value so obtained was then multiplied by the relevant weighting factor as given in ICRP 1977.

tics, the type of radiation safety procedures and how well they are carried out, and the training and experience of the personnel involved. Representative data for dose equivalent per procedure from one institution are shown in Table 6.2. This information is reproduced here to illustrate the type of information that is useful in implementing an ALARA program and should not be interpreted as limits or goals for any institution.

To illustrate the use of reference ranges in a cardiac catheterization laboratory ALARA program, consider the following hypothetical example. A busy cardiac facility performs approximately 1,000 cardiac catheterizations, 200 pacemaker implants and 40 angioplasties per year in a facility having two cardiac imaging suites staffed by five cardiologists, five radiologic technologists and four nurses. Radiation monitors are routinely worn on the collar outside of protective apparel and, therefore, reference ranges are set on the basis of these readings rather than on the basis of under-apron monitors or a calculated whole body effective dose equivalent. A review of monitoring records reveals yearly average dose equivalents of 26 mSv; all staff are measurably exposed with cardiologists and nurses typically receiving higher doses and technologists receiving lower doses. The annual collective dose equivalent is 370 person-mSv. From a review of quarterly monitoring reports, it was noted that the average quarterly dose equivalent was 6.5 mSv and that 95 percent of personnel received less than 16 mSv. The quarterly collective dose equivalent was 93 ± 12 person-mSv with the fluctuation being due primarily to workload. Following the procedures outlined in Section 4.3, the individual reference range (IRR) was set from 6.5 to 16 mSv/qtr and the collective reference range (CRR) was set from 105 to 117 person-mSv/qtr. Other institutions with different equipment, workload and staffing might set different action levels.

6.3 Hypothetical Examples of Optimization Decisions in Implementing ALARA

6.3.1 *Elevated Exposures in a Cardiac Catheterization Laboratory*

A large general hospital which served also as a teaching institution housed a particularly active cardiology service. There were three cardiac catheterization laboratories, each containing a normal complement of equipment. The workload in these laboratories averaged approximately five cases each day in each laboratory, for a total of 3,800 procedures per year, and greater than 90 percent of the patients were adults. The personnel complement included twelve staff cardiologists and four resident cardiologists. The technical staff numbered thirty-four and almost all cases were supported by anesthesiologists or nurse anesthetists.

Each member of the cardiac catheterization team was monitored for radiation exposure. All personnel who remained in the room during procedures producing exposure received protective aprons of 0.5 mm lead equivalent. Frequently, an assistant would be positioned facing away from the x-ray examination table. In such cases, either the apron was worn backwards or a wraparound apron was provided.

In setting up the ALARA program, it was decided to have the radiation monitoring service print the monitoring records of cardiology separately from the rest of monitored employees so that any trends in exposure patterns would be more readily apparent. From a review of quarterly reports, the individual reference range was set at 5.5 to 12.5 mSv while the collective reference range was set at 220 to 240 person-mSv. Typical results from quarterly reviews showed that imaging physician dose equivalents fell within the IRR, while technologist dose equivalents fell near or below the IRR. This pattern was consistent with the known characteristics of catheterization laboratories, in which imaging physicians account for the largest fraction of dose equivalent.

Upon review of quarterly collective dose and procedure volume data, it became apparent that the collective dose over the past several review periods was increasing towards the upper limit of the CRR even though no individuals exceeded the IRR and the workload was roughly constant. Hence, a trend was identified and an investigation initiated. A more detailed review of monitor records revealed that the bulk of the increase was due to the exposure of residents and cardiologists. To identify the source of the increase the annual radiation control records as well as calibration and quality assurance records of each room were reviewed. No equipment-related sources of increased exposure were identified. Protective equipment such as ceiling suspended scatter shields were in place and being utilized.

The next approach proposed by the Radiation Safety Office (RSO) was to obtain some direct reading pencil dosimeters. These were issued to residents and cardiologists on those days that they were in the catheterization laboratory. The routine for this service was for the staff cardiologists to perform procedures in the imaging laboratory on alternate days so that the use of the pencil dosimeters had to be followed carefully to avoid use of the dosimeters by the wrong personnel.

The results of this monitoring were unremarkable. The pencil readings verified the level of exposure reported on the monthly monitors. There were no obvious or significant differences among either the three rooms or the sixteen cardiologists, although exposures of residents were somewhat higher than those of staff.

Next, the RSO devoted one entire week to monitoring each individual procedure by component—radiographic, fluoroscopic and cine. A single dosimeter was used for each of the components. It was quickly apparent that the component exposure for a single procedure was too low to be assessed accurately. Therefore, individual dosimeters were passed along from cardiologist to cardiologist during the day for each component of a procedure in a given room. The data clearly showed that although the cine portion of the examination occupied the least time during a 0.5 to 2.0 hour procedure, it accounted for approximately 75 percent of the cardiologists' exposure. This result was consistent with published reports. The data also showed that the average dose equivalent per procedure was approximately 0.3 mSv rather than an average of 0.2 mSv which had been achieved in past years.

The net result of the investigation was to focus on procedures and training as the best possible response, since all equipment and shielding were operating and utilized properly. Hence, a staff meeting was called to discuss the results of the investigation and explore possible actions. To reinforce awareness of radiation safety, the characteristics of radiation sources and levels in the catheterization labs were presented and the staff invited to suggest possible ways of reducing exposure.

The staff acknowledged that there might have been a tendency to perform longer cine runs with more being conducted at 60 frames per second (fps) rather than at 30 fps. The consensus was that a concerted effort to use the shortest cine time and lowest frame rate consistent with good patient care was appropriate. Inasmuch as the reported occupational exposures were not alarmingly high, restrictions on technique were rejected. The importance of maximizing distance from the patient during cineradiography was also reiterated. To foster awareness of exposure levels, it was also decided to post monitoring reports, grouped according to cardiologists, residents, technologists and other. All of these actions incurred no costs, hence, dose reductions would certainly be cost-beneficial.

The result of this approach to a rather nebulous problem was the reversal of a trend. During the next several quarterly review periods, a slow but steady decline in collective dose equivalent and average dose equivalent was noted. This exercise in implementing ALARA did not hinge on an abrupt finding or an abrupt solution. Rather, the reduction in occupational exposure resulted from a rededication to concerted radiation control.

6.3.2 *Radiation Monitoring of Operating Room Nurses*

The Director of Radiology in a 150-bed suburban hospital received a request from the nursing supervisor to provide radiation monitors for all nurses who assisted in the operating room during procedures involving a newly acquired mobile C-arm fluoroscope. Two orthopedic surgeons had recently joined the existing staff of three already practicing at the hospital and after the arrival of the mobile C-arm fluoroscope, they instituted several new procedures. The nursing staff responded by expressing considerable concern for their radiation safety.

Being unfamiliar with what air kerma levels to expect, and unwilling to incur the expense and administrative overhead of monitoring all operating room personnel, the director reviewed the literature and consulted with a neighboring hospital that had been performing mobile C-arm orthopedic procedures for several years. Based upon this information, and projecting a workload of approximately 300 procedures per year, it was anticipated that the two technologists operating the mobile C-arm fluoroscope might receive dose equivalents ranging from 2 to 5 mSv/y while physician dose equivalents might range from 1 to 6 mSv/y.

In view of these projected occupational exposures to orthopedic surgeons and technologists, it was deemed reasonable to provide radiation monitors for nursing personnel on a trial basis, while at the same time evaluating whether this would be necessary on a long-term basis. Thirty-two nurses were provided with radiation monitors. To help evaluate and interpret the results, a record book was also initiated in which date, patient name, physician name, procedure type, fluoroscopic time and number of radiographs were recorded.

After the first three months of this program, it became apparent that the C-arm was being used most frequently for restructuring the hip. An evaluation of its use showed that an average of six procedures were conducted each week and about half of these involved the hip. The remainder of the workload was split among catheter insertions, pacemaker insertions and closed reductions. At the end of the initial six month monitoring period, 90 percent of the monitors assigned to nurses indicated no measurable occupational dose equivalent; the remaining 10 percent never exceeded 2.5 µSv in any one month, and the largest quarterly total was 0.5 mSv. The five radiologic technologists assigned to this service had dose equivalents ranging from 1.5 to 7 mSv. These reported dose equivalents resulted from monitors worn at the collar level above the protective apron. They also reflected the technologists' exposure from other departmental activities.

The cost of providing monthly radiation monitors to 32 nurses for one year was estimated to be $500, while the total collective dose monitored was estimated to be less than 4 person-mSv. Even if nursing exposure were reduced to zero, the cost of demonstrating this through monthly monitoring would be greater than $125,000/person-Sv ($500 per year divided by 0.004 person-Sv). The choice was whether to monitor nurses on a less frequent basis (i.e., quarterly) or not at all. In this case, it was decided not to monitor nurses, but to provide the nursing supervisor with the monitor reports of the technologists and orthopedic surgeons so that all would be satisfied that the radiation environment had not changed from that found at the time of the study.

An ancillary, and perhaps more useful, finding of this study was the wide range of techniques employed by the various orthopedic surgeons. For instance, the range of exposures required for a hip pinning varied from two minutes to 27 minutes of fluoroscopy time. What became particularly apparent was that two out of eight orthopedic surgeons accounted for 60 percent of the beam-on workload. For example, during emplacement of a hip prosthesis, they averaged 11.6 minutes of fluoroscopy time compared to 4.2 minutes for the others. It appeared that some were not taking full advantage of the image-store capabilities of the equipment.

This disparity was brought to the attention of all five of the orthopedic surgeons by way of a memorandum which listed the workload for each type of procedure and for each surgeon during the six month monitoring period. In this way, it was apparent to all that there were two surgeons responsible for the bulk of the exposure. Once this situation was publicized, all physicians, not just the two surgeons reduced their x-ray workload per procedure. Already low occupational exposures were reduced further.

6.3.3 *Occupational Exposures During Computed Tomography*

A separate imaging center was staffed by two radiologists and twelve technologists. This center contained all of the available imaging modalities. It included a radiographic-fluoroscopic room, a radiographic-tomographic room, and equipment for mammography, ultrasound, nuclear medicine, computed tomography and magnetic resonance imaging. The center operated five days a week, ten hours each day with moderate patient loads. The technologists at this imaging center were compartmentalized; that is, they serviced the same area each day with very little switching or substituting. The technologists assigned to computed tomography showed sporadic exposures ranging from minimal to 0.5 mSv per month. There were four technologists operating two CT scanners and their reported dose equivalents for the previous year were 1.2, 1.8, 2.6 and 2 mSv resulting in a collective dose equivalent of 7.6 person-mSv. The quarterly mean dose equivalent was approximately 0.5 mSv. Due to the few data, meaningful dose equivalent distributions could not be constructed so the lower and upper bounds of the IRR were set at the quarterly average and 3 times the quarterly average dose equivalent as discussed in Section 4.3. Similarly, there were insufficient data to calculate the normal fluctuation in collective dose equivalent. However, a 20 percent quarterly fluctuation was assumed to be reasonable. Thus, the quarterly IRR was set to 0.5 to 1.5 mSv and the quarterly CRR at 2.3 to 2.7 person-mSv.

A review of monitoring records showed that one technologist received a quarterly total of 1.8 mSv thus triggering an automatic investigation. It was unclear whether these occupational exposures were being received while operating the scanners or attending the patients during examinations. Interviews conducted with the technologists revealed that elevated film badge readings correlated with months in which they imaged patients that required a technologist to remain in the CT room during the scan. During such procedures, a protective apron was worn. However, at this imaging center, standard procedure was to position the radiation monitor at collar level above the protective apron. Therefore, it was suspected that most of the reported occupational exposures might be due to this in-room activity.

To confirm the situation, a number of area radiation monitors were obtained from the radiation monitor vendor. Several were placed inside the room at waist level on the walls. Where possible, a companion monitor was positioned on the outside of the barrier. Others were placed at the control booth barrier, on the wall, on the view window and at the operating console. A six-month sampling of these data resulted in the values given in Table 6.3.

TABLE 6.3—*Example of area monitoring results for computed tomography rooms (average monthly dose equivalent).*

	Room 1		Room 2	
	Inside (mSv)	Outside (mSv)	Inside (mSv)	Outside (mSv)
Wall A	0.42	<0.1	3.26	1.82
Wall B	2.58	1.25	1.44	0.55
Wall C	1.12	0.45	0.38	0.18
Control booth barrier	0.68	0.28	1.10	0.40
Technologist barrier	0.12		0.16	

It was clear from these data that the walls were not lead-lined and the view window was not leaded glass. The data, however, indicated that the barriers as constructed were adequate. The exposures recorded in the control booth area and at the technologists' position were much too low to account for the higher than expected occupational exposures reported.

Options considered in response to the situation were "take no action" and "modify shielding." It was impossible to modify the imaging procedures since some patients would always require in-room personnel. Because the dose equivalents were received by the eye and thyroid, it was possible to provide lead thyroid collars and face shields at a cost of approximately $400. This was not given full consideration because the technologists said they likely would not wear them and expressed concern that the patients might find such shields to be disturbing. A mobile barrier with a clear leaded plastic viewing window was available at a cost of $800. If able to be used on 70 percent of in-room cases, the shield was estimated to result in a collective-dose reduction of 5 person-mSv to the head and neck region. The effective whole body collective-dose reduction may be 20 percent of this, depending upon organ weighting factors and the transmission coefficient of the lead apron. Over a ten-year lifetime, the cost per person-Sv was thus estimated to be between $6,000 and $30,000. This figure was judged cost effective and the shield was purchased.

7. Implementation of ALARA in Nuclear Medicine

7.1 Sources of External Occupational Exposure in Nuclear Medicine

An understanding of how radiation exposure occurs is basic to the success of efforts to optimize radiation protection. Nuclear medicine personnel are exposed to ionizing radiation primarily during radiopharmaceutical preparation and assay, radiopharmaceutical administration, and imaging procedures. Each procedure poses unique radiation safety issues.

7.1.1 *Radiopharmaceutical Preparation and Assay*

The use of radionuclide generators, particularly the prevalent molybdenum-99-technetium-99m generator, results in the handling of tens of GBq of radioactive material during elution of the generator. The magnitude of the resulting exposure depends upon the procedures and precautions followed. Barrall and Smith (1976) studied the exposure patterns to personnel when performing some common clinical nuclear medicine procedures.[3] Their results are shown in Table 7.1. The data are for procedures of average difficulty in typical patients. Syringe shields were used when performing injections. Exposure to personnel occurs primarily because of their close proximity to the patient, for example while positioning the patient and camera to obtain a series of views to cover the area of interest. In the last column of Table 7.1 is listed the percentage of the total exposure resulting from the imaging process itself. For the institutions in this study, radiopharmaceutical preparation and assay usu-

---

[3]In several locations in this section, occupational exposures are listed for specific nuclear medicine procedures. In some cases these exposures reflect the experience of one or a few institutions and may not represent average exposures nationally or exposures consistent with ALARA levels.

TABLE 7.1—*Typical dose equivalents to nuclear medicine personnel from selected procedures (after Barrall and Smith, 1976).*

Procedure	Activity injected[a] Tc-99m (MBq)	Dose equivalent			Total (μSv)	Percent of exposure from imaging
		Dose preparation & assay[a] (μSv)	Injection[a] (μSv)	Imaging (μSv)		
Brain scan	740	0.4	0.2	2.2	2.8	79
Cerebral blood flow (CBF) study	740	0.4	0.2	0.3	0.9	33
CBF & brain study	740	0.4	0.2	2.5	3.1	81
Liver & spleen scan	148	0.1	0.1	0.3	0.5	60
Bone scan (recti-linear scanner)	555	0.2	0.1	0.6	0.9	67
Bone scan (camera)	555	0.2	0.1	5.4	5.7	95
Thyroid scan	74	0.2	0.1	0.4	0.7	57
Myocardial scan	555	0.1	0.1	0.2	0.4	50
Radionuclide Angiography	370	0.2	0.1	0.4	0.7	57

[a]Syringe shields were used

ally contribute a smaller fraction of the exposure from the entire procedure, with imaging contributing the major fraction. The exception to this rule is cerebral blood flow studies, because the imaging time for these procedures is usually quite short. The data of Table 7.1 may not be universally applicable. For instance, Ahluwalia *et al.* (1981) reported a significant reduction in personnel exposure when unit dose radiopharmaceuticals were prepared by a centralized radiopharmacy. This seems to indicate that preparation and assay had contributed a larger fraction of personnel exposure than might be expected from Table 7.1.

A report by Iyer and Dhond (1980) revealed a general trend toward increased exposure of personnel working with generator-produced radionuclides as compared with exposure of personnel not working with generators. In a more recent survey of several hospitals of various sizes in a metropolitan area, a savings in personnel exposure resulted with a switch from individual generators to a centralized radiopharmacy. Dose equivalents to the whole body averaged 1.95 mSv per 1000 procedures for the radiopharmacy use versus 3.42 mSv per 1000 procedures for generator use. Extremity dose equivalents averaged 8.28 mSv per 1000 procedures for the radiopharmacy use versus 18.5 mSv per 1000 procedures for generator use.[4]

7.1.2 *Radiopharmaceutical Administration*

The handling of radiopharmaceuticals can cause high exposure rates, particularly to extremities. With an unshielded syringe, extremity air kerma rates of 6 mGy/h-MBq to the tip of the second finger and 10 mGy/h-MBq to the index finger have been measured (Barrall and Smith, 1976). The bulkiness and added weight of the syringe shield makes injection of radiopharmaceuticals more difficult. However, a survey of physicians and technologists showed essentially no difference in the time needed for injection, with or without a syringe shield (Branson *et al.*, 1976). The same report notes that exposure to the users' hands while preparing radiopharmaceuticals can be reduced by as much as 50 percent by the use of syringe shields; the maximum reduction to the hands of a person administering activity to a patient can be as high as 80 to 90 percent. The use of syringe shields has been demonstrated to reduce exposure levels by a factor of three or more (Branson *et al.*, 1977). The data of Table 7.1 indicate that injection using syringe shields may contribute from

[4]Personal communication from James G. Kereiakes, Professor of Radiology, University of Cincinnati.

2 percent (in the case of a bone scan) to 25 percent (for myocardial imaging) of the occupational dose equivalent from a procedure.

7.1.3 *Imaging*

The patient is a source of radiation; hence, the imaging time and distance from the patient are important determinants of personnel exposure. The use of short-lived radionuclides presents a reduced hazard to the patient, but, because of higher activities administered, a greater radiation risk to the technologist. In recent years, many nuclear medicine facilities have added new imaging equipment to handle an increasing patient workload without providing a proportionate increase in space. As a consequence, imaging rooms are more confined and exposure to the technologists has increased. A correlation between higher annual dose equivalents and limited work space has been reported (Barrall *et al.*, 1978). Ancillary equipment such as video monitors, computer terminals, exercise equipment, cardiac monitoring modules, and critical care systems may also contribute to the crowding, thus making nuclear medicine personnel less able to keep distant from patients undergoing imaging. The data of Table 7.1 indicate that a significant fraction of whole body exposure may be received during imaging. Radiation dose rates associated with radioactive patients undergoing bone and brain imaging studies have been measured by Brahmavar *et al.* (1984). For an average activity of approximately 700 MBq per patient, the average air kerma level was 200 μGy h^{-1} at the patient's surface and 40 μGy h^{-1} at 12 inches from the surface. Brahmavar *et al.* (1984) also estimated average annual radiation dose to technologists of 4 mGy to the fingertips and 2 mGy to the whole body resulting from proximity to radioactive patients. These values were based on 1000 procedures per year with an average of 700 MBq activity each. An air kerma rate of 200 μGy h^{-1} and an exposure time of one minute per procedure is given for the fingertip values. The whole body exposure values are based on an air kerma rate of 10 μGy h^{-1} and an exposure time of ten minutes per procedure.

Before nuclear cardiology procedures became a significant fraction of workload, Gandsman *et al.* (1980) suggested that brain studies accounted for most of the radiation exposure to technologists. This is in agreement with the data of Barrall and Smith (1976) presented in Table 7.1. With the advent of nuclear cardiology, Gandsman *et al.* (1984) updated their observations and reported a significant increase in exposure levels due to this study. Personnel exposure from nuclear cardiovascular procedures has been investigated by Syed *et al.*

(1982). Air kerma rates at the couch edge from a patient given 1100 MBq of ^{99m}Tc MDA (methylene diphosphonate) ranged from 6 μGy h^{-1} to 25 μGy h^{-1}. For 200 MBq of ^{99m}Tc HSA (human serum albumin) air kerma rates ranged from 2 μGy h^{-1} to 20 μGy h^{-1}. Typical total exposure per procedure was not reported.

7.1.4 Sources of Internal Occupational Exposure in Nuclear Medicine

Internal occupational exposure of personnel occurs through inadvertent ingestion and inhalation of radioisotopes and absorption through the skin. For facilities following standard radiation safety practices, internal exposure should be much less than external. However, internal exposure presents special circumstances in that it is not detected by a personal monitor and is, therefore, not normally monitored on an individual basis. Internal exposure is controlled by limiting contamination of work surfaces and room air, and potential for exposure is monitored by area wipe tests and air sampling. Some medical centers conduct routine bioassays as a method of monitoring internal exposure.

Internal exposure from ^{99m}Tc contamination has been studied by Nishiyama et al. (1980a, 1980b). The major pathway for internal deposition was hand-to-mouth contamination, primarily during radiopharmaceutical preparation, rather than during injection and imaging. No evidence was found for inhalation of airborne radiopharmaceuticals. The total body absorbed dose for the most heavily contaminated personnel was estimated to be approximately 2.5 μGy/y.

Internal exposure from therapeutic doses of ^{131}I has been studied by Nishiyama et al. (1980c). The high volatility of iodine may result in internal exposure via inhalation. Whole body activity burdens were observed to range from 3 to 230 Bq per GBq of administered radionuclide, depending on type of radiopharmaceuticals used and whether fume hoods were used for handling. For a therapeutic dose of 3700 MBq, assuming a thyroid uptake of 20 percent, the thyroid dose to the technologist per therapeutic procedure could range from 0.008 to 7.1 mGy.

Ventilation studies also present the chance of internal exposure through inhalation of airborne contamination. Nishiyama and Lukes (1982) have studied personnel exposure from ^{133}Xe procedures in three representative hospitals. The inspired activity ranged from approximately 2 to 200 kBq during a typical 20-minute study. The wide range of exposure depended primarily on the xenon exhaust and trapping systems, with air flow, room exchange rates and degree of patient cooperation being additional factors. If the same technologist performs five ventilation-perfusion studies per week for 50 weeks per year, the estimated annual absorbed dose to the lung would range from 0.04 to 4 µGy/y at the institutions studied.

7.1.5 Exposure of Other Personnel from Patients Receiving Diagnostic Radionuclides

Nursing personnel are exposed to low-level radiation from patients receiving diagnostic radionuclides. In a study by Burks et al. (1982), nurses were monitored by film badges and self-reading pocket dosimeters while caring for patients who received diagnostic radionuclides. Most patients in the study were ambulatory and required 3 to 6 nursing care contact hours per day. Over 13 weeks, a total of 73 patients underwent 194 diagnostic radionuclide studies. Eight different diagnostic radionuclides were administered in doses ranging from 15 to 1000 MBq. The ^{133}Xe used for lung ventilation scans did not contribute to dosimeter readings. The highest cumulative quarterly dose equivalent recorded was 0.11 ± 0.1 mSv/qtr.

Brateman et al. (1980) calculated exposures to the hands and gonads of ultrasonographers in contact with 25 patients who received diagnostic radionuclides. Ultrasonographers often spend 20 to 90 minutes in close contact with patients who have received diagnostic radionuclides from 0 to 5 days before the ultrasound procedure. Calculated air kerma to the ultrasonographers range from 10 to 400 µGy to the hands and from 3 µGy to 70 µGy to the gonads.

7.2 Normative Patterns of Occupational Exposure and Workload, and Indicators for Suspicion of Non-ALARA Situations

Several reports have been published concerning the patterns of exposure received by nuclear medicine personnel (Barrall and Smith, 1976; Anger, 1977; Gandsman et al., 1980; Ahluwalia et al., 1981; Gandsman et al., 1984; Brahmavar et al., 1984). While some reports provide ranges of exposures, the distribution of exposures (which is expected to be log-normal) has not been widely reported. All of the discussions concerned personnel engaged solely in nuclear medicine, i.e., exposure from diagnostic radiology procedures did not contribute to the total. With the possible exception of dedicated radiopharmacy personnel, most tasks in nuclear medicine are not subspecialized; hence the reported exposure patterns are not divided by subcategory of worker. Average yearly whole body and extremity dose equivalents are summarized in Table 7.2. Reported average whole body dose-equivalents ranged from 1.9 to 8 mSv/y. Since only two of the reports include workload data, it is not possible to decide if the variation in exposure is due more to staffing patterns, radiation safety practices, or workload. A ten-year summary from one of the institutions is shown in Figure 7.1 (Gandsman et al., 1984). The number of technologists monitored was four (1973–1974), five (1974–1980) and six (1980–1982). Hence, the average whole body exposure was affected both by the number of staff and the workload per unit staff. Analysis of the data reveals that from 1973 to 1977 true gains were made in terms of reducing the whole body exposure per number of procedures. After 1976, the dose equivalent per procedure increased gradually from 1.5 to 2.1 μSv. Hence, the rise in average whole body exposure from 1978 to 1980 was due both to an increased number of procedures and to an increased occupational exposure per procedure.

Few firm conclusions can be drawn from the available studies. None of the hospitals reported in the literature exceeded an average whole body dose equivalent of 8 mSv/y for monitored personnel; many hospitals reported lower values. The contribution to average annual whole body dose equivalent per procedure ranged from 1.3 to 4.1 mSv at one institution (Gandsman et al., 1984). The data of Gandsman et al. (1984) are consistent with the dose equivalent/ procedure values of individual procedures reported by Barrall and Smith (1976) and reproduced in Table 7.1. However, too few data exist to allow calculation of values of dose equivalent/procedure that would be representative of national norms. Until such data become available, a retrospective analysis of each institution's own data may serve as a starting point.

As an example of how normative patterns may be used to set reference levels, consider the following hypothetical situation. The nuclear medicine section of a large hospital is staffed by four technologists and performs 5,000 procedures per year. From a review of their past several years of quarterly film badge totals, it was determined that less than five percent of quarterly individual doses exceeded 2.5 mSv while the average measurable quarterly dose was 0.9 mSv. Radiation protection surveys were also reviewed and typical, as well as maximal, quarterly doses were calculated based on workload and staffing patterns. From this review it was determined that, most of the time, personnel should be able to carry out their normal duties without exceeding a quarterly individual dose of 2.5 mSv. Based upon these considerations the quarterly individual reference range (IRR) was set at 0.9 mSv to 2.5 mSv. A similar review of

TABLE 7.2—*Results of various studies of average yearly dose equivalent of nuclear medicine personnel.*

Average whole body dose equivalent (mSv/y)	Average extremity dose equivalent (mSv/y)	Average workload per worker (studies/y)	Reference
4.78[a]	NR	NR	Barrall and Smith, 1976
7.9	NR	NR	Anger, 1977
1.8	5.25	1200	Gandsman et al., 1980
8[b]	NR	NR	Ahluwalia et al., 1981
2.8[c]			
3	18	1400	Gandsman et al., 1984
7	NR	NR	Brahmavar et al., 1984

[a]average of 47 hospitals
[b]before initiation of centralized radiopharmacy
[c]after initiation of centralized radiopharmacy
NR = not reported

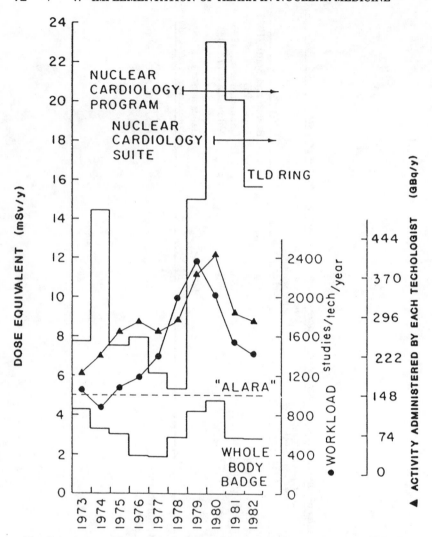

Fig. 7.1 Average dose equivalent in mSv/y during the years 1973 to 1982. The lowest solid line represents the whole-body data and the uppermost solid line represents the ring badge data. The concurrent work load per technologist (studies per technologist per year) is represented by circles and the total activity administered by each technologist (GBq per year) is shown as triangles (After Gandsman *et al.*, 1984). The "ALARA" level (dotted line) is an action level chosen by Gandsman *et al.* for this particular set of circumstances.

quarterly collective dose records, corrected for trends in work-load, revealed that the average quarterly collective dose was approximately 3.8 0.3 person-mSv. These data were used to set the collective reference range (CRR) at 4.1 to 4.4 person-mSv.

7.3 Hypothetical Examples of Optimization Decisions in Implementing ALARA

7.3.1 *Radiopharmacy vs. Generator Use*

As an example of the manner in which an ALARA program might be implemented for nuclear medicine personnel, consider the following hypothetical example: A newly opened nuclear medicine section of a community hospital, with three technologists, hopes to achieve a workload of 3000 procedures per year. Lacking retrospective exposure data of its own, the institution used literature values, such as those reviewed in the previous section, to set reference levels. It was anticipated that the average yearly whole body dose should be approximately 3 mSv to 4 mSv. The mean dose equivalent per quarter was thus anticipated to be 1 mSv/qtr. The lower limit of the IRR was set at 1 mSv/qtr and the upper at 3 mSv/qtr, following the general guidlines discussed in Section 4.3. Similarly, it was expected that the collective dose per procedure should be between 2 and 5 person-μSv which, for the projected workload, results in a yearly expected collective dose equivalent between 6 and 15 person-mSv per year. For consistency with the anticipated average yearly whole body dose a yearly collective dose of 12 person-mSv was used, for a quarterly collective dose of 3 person-mSv. The quarterly CRR awaits accurate data, but was set with a lower bound of 3 person-mSv and an upper bound of 4 person-mSv based upon the expectation that quarterly fluctuation in workload should not exceed 30 percent of the average workload.

During each of the first two quarterly review periods the IRR was nearly exceeded by one technologist, but not by the same technologist both times. The quarterly collective doses were 3.95 and 4.3 person-mSv, and the number of procedures performed was 575 and 650. This presents an equivocal data set upon which to decide whether ALARA is being achieved. With so few individuals being monitored the elevated individual readings could be normal fluctuations due to patterns of work assignments or the reading could indicate a need for further action. The collective dose figures do not appear to be unreasonable, particularly since no historical data from the institution are available for comparison. However, the average contribution to collective dose per procedure is 6.7 μSv, which is above expectations. Since the elevated individual quarterly doses were not commensurate with the workload, it was decided to proceed with further investigation.

The investigation consisted of a review and observation of procedures and measurements of exposure levels during the various phases of the procedures to determine site specific data analogous to that presented in Table 7.1. Exposure levels near the patient during imaging were found to be similar to those reported in the literature. Proper procedures were followed to maximize distance from the patient and minimize time spent near the patient. The simple suggestion of Gandsman *et al.* (1980) to cover non-essential areas of the patient with a lead apron was found to further reduce exposure levels during many procedures. The investigation then focused on elution and dose preparation as the potential problem. As expected, the instantaneous exposure rates during the various steps of elution and radiopharmaceutical preparation were quite high. From these measurements and from literature reports of dose reductions achieved through modifications of radiopharmacy operations, it was hypothesized that this segment of the overall imaging procedure might be responsible for the observed personnel monitor readings.

The possible actions considered were "take no action", review and revise the procedures used to elute and prepare radiopharmaceuticals, and contracting with a commercial radiopharmacy instead of in-house generation and preparation of radiopharmaceuticals. Additional shielding was not considered because appropriate shielding was already in place. Reviewing and revising procedures was estimated to cost approximately three person-weeks from the combined efforts of the radiation safety officer, chief technologist and nuclear medicine physician. Whether or not this represents a real cost to the department is problematic since these are salaried individuals and actual outlay of the department does not change as a result of the manner in which they allocate their time. Additional problems encountered with the proposed procedural changes were whether they would be effective and reluctance to change procedures that already followed accepted standards of practice.

The costs of changing to a commercial radiopharmacy could be more directly evaluated. Generators cost $350 each, and the average cost of the pharmaceutical was about $12 per vial. The costs of receipt and handling of generators, associated record keeping, time spent preparing technetium-labeled radiopharmaceuticals and time spent on associated quality assurance were estimated to be $1500 per quarter. The cost of commercial radiopharmaceuticals delivered in unit dose form ready for injection was estimated to be about $15 per vial for the types and number of procedures being done; charges averaged $540 per month for general delivery and $340 per month for special delivery. Less well known were the costs associated with wastage and availability. The best estimate of the net cost of switching to a commercial radiopharmacy was estimated to be about $2000 per year. The anticipated reduction in average personnel dose equivalent was estimated not to exceed 6 mSv/year, based upon the experience of other institutions as published in the literature. The resulting cost of $110,000 per person-Sv was judged to be acceptable by the institution and it was decided to use the commercial radiopharmacy on a trial basis and evaluate the impact of the change not only upon personnel exposure but also upon the quality of care delivered to the nuclear medicine patients, particularly with added technologists' time from not having to prepare the radiopharmaceutical.

An issue not addressed by the above analysis is the exposure to the employees of the commercial radiopharmacy or transport workers. If the exposure avoided by the hospital nuclear medicine employees is simply transferred to the employees of the commercial radiopharmacy, then the overall collective dose would remain the same. Exposure would be reduced in one group at the expense of increased exposure to another group. In the above example, the hospital did not have detailed information about radiation protection practices of the commercial radiopharmacy, but assumed that the commercial radiopharmacy could prepare its products in a more exposure-efficient manner due to its greater facilities and more experienced personnel. Ideally the commercial radiopharmacy would include the cost of radiation protection in the cost of its product so that issues of this nature would be resolved as part of the cost-benefit analysis.

7.3.2 *Patient Imaging Procedures-Nuclear Cardiology*

This example follows the data given by Gandsman *et al.* (1984) and indicates how an ALARA program may function as new procedures are implemented in nuclear medicine laboratories. From 1976–1978, personnel exposures had stabilized at an individual whole body dose equivalent of 2 mSv/year. This figure was used to project a quarterly IRR of 0.25 mSv to 0.75 mSv. From 1978–1980, a significant increase was observed in the individual dose equivalent level to 1.2 mSv/quarter. The IRR had been exceeded. Upon reviewing the workload, it was noted that this increase in exposure coincided with the development of the nuclear cardiology program. Despite a decrease in workload (number of procedures per year) the increase reflected the use of greater amounts of administered radiopharmaceuticals and a greater personnel time commitment for the nuclear cardiology studies. Since each technologist rotated through the cardiology program, this increase also represented an increase in the collective dose.

In response to this increased demand for nuclear cardiology studies, an area was renovated as a dedicated suite with a design goal of minimizing personnel exposures. Two rooms were renovated, an imaging room (15 × 20 ft) containing the gamma camera, patient care equipment and supplies, and an adjoining computer room (10 × 10 ft) connected to the imaging room and having a large observation window. This allowed monitoring of the patients during the data acquisition while minimizing staff exposure. The cost of this renovation was $12,500. Personnel dose decreased between 1981 and 1982 to about 0.5 mSv/quarter, within the previously set quarterly IRR. For the five technologists involved, the renovation represented a collective dose decrease from 24 person-mSv/year to 10 person-mSv/year. The resulting $90,000 cost per person-Sv was judged acceptable by the institution.

8. Implementation of ALARA in Radiation Oncology

8.1 Sources of Occupational Exposure in Radiation Oncology

There are three major categories of activities in radiation oncology that may expose personnel to radiation: brachytherapy, external beam treatment and therapy simulation.

8.1.1 *Brachytherapy*

The most significant source of radiation exposure to radiation oncology personnel is the use of sealed radionuclide sources in brachytherapy (unsealed sources were treated in Section 7). The most commonly used isotopes are ^{137}Cs, ^{192}Ir, ^{226}Ra and ^{125}I, although ^{60}Co, ^{90}Sr and ^{198}Au and several other isotopes are used occasionally. Physicists and technologists may be exposed during the receipt and preparation of brachytherapy sources. Physicians, anesthetists and operating room nurses may be exposed during the loading and unloading of sources. During the course of treatment, nurses will be occupationally exposed. For a radiation oncology center offering both external beam therapy and brachytherapy treatments, it is usually the brachytherapy procedures which account for the greatest fraction of individual exposure and collective dose (Hughes *et al.*, 1983; Leung, 1983).

8.1.2 *External Beam Units*

Technologists and, to a lesser extent, physicians and physicists may be exposed to radiation from various external beam units. Radiation therapy units are sources of primary, scattered (from the patient) and leakage (through the machine "head") radiation that can expose personnel after penetrating the shielding of the treatment room. As with all external beam therapy equipment, personnel should not be present in the treatment room during the actual treatment with the possible exception of the use of low energy (50 kVp and below) x-ray contact therapy units which are sometimes used for intracavitary treatments. Cobalt-60 teletherapy units can expose personnel to head leakage radiation while the source is in the "off" position, and to primary, scattered, and leakage radiation that penetrates the protective barrier when the source is in the "on" position. The types of exposure from linear accelerators, betatrons and microtrons depend upon the beam modality (photon or electron) and the beam energy. For photons and electrons below 10 MeV, the only radiations are primary, scattered, and leakage x rays that penetrate the protective barrier.

Above 10 MeV, photonuclear reactions can result in the production of both neutrons and radioactive nuclides (activation products). Neutrons can penetrate the protective barrier and expose personnel when the unit is on. Relatively long-lived radionuclides produced by photoactivation can expose personnel who enter the treatment room immediately after the treatment has been delivered. Neutrons and photoactivated radionuclides usually do not contribute a significant fraction of the exposure to technologists except for units operated at very high energy ($\geq$ 25 MV x ray)[(Hoffman and Nath, 1982; NCRP, 1984; McGinley et al., 1984; La Riviere, 1985)]. Barrier penetration by primary, scattered, and leakage radiation depends upon the characteristics of the accelerator and the design of the facility. As will be seen in Section 8.2, the average yearly doses to personnel who work only with megavoltage x-ray external beam equipment rarely exceed a few mSv/y.

8.1.3 Therapy Simulation

Technologists, physicians and physicists may be exposed to low energy x rays from simulators and other diagnostic imaging equipment used to plan treatments. Fluoroscopic simulation protocols that require the presence of personnel near the patient during imaging may produce relatively high levels of scattered radiation because therapy simulators often use high radiation output to compensate for a large patient-to-image receptor distance. In the United States, fluoroscopic simulators are exempt from the Federal maximum exposure rate regulations normally limiting the maximum entrance rate for diagnostic fluoroscopic equipment. Also, the geometry of the simulator may not be compatible with protective drapery. However, for the majority of fluoroscopic simulations, and nearly all radiographic simulations, personnel are located in a shielded control area. Unlike diagnostic fluoroscopic equipment, the x-ray beam need not be collimated to the input size of the image receptor; hence it is necessary to shield therapy simulation rooms with primary radiation barriers. As will be seen in the next section, simulation is typically not a major contributor to the total radiation exposure of radiation oncology personnel.

8.2 Normative Patterns of Occupational Exposure and Workload and Indicators for Suspicion of Non-ALARA Situations

Several reports have been published concerning the types and patterns of exposure[5] received by radiation oncology personnel (Hoffman & Nath, 1982; Leung, 1983; Hughes *et al.*, 1983; Cobb *et al.*, 1978). The distribution of exposures is approximately log normal for radiation oncology workers as a whole as well as for the various subcategories of these workers. Because the subcategories show considerable variation in the average annual dose and collective dose per unit workload, it is preferable to consider each individually.

8.2.1 *Personnel Involved Primarily in Brachytherapy*

The magnitude and distribution of exposure among persons involved with brachytherapy depend on individual institutional practices. A study of British brachytherapy workers found that the total collective dose due to brachytherapy was distributed as follows: 67 percent to ward nurses, 11 percent to operating room nurses, 8 percent to radiotherapists, 7 percent to source laboratory staff (staff responsible for receipt and preparation of brachytherapy sources) and the remainder distributed among several other categories of workers (Hughes *et al.*, 1983). Operating room nurses and source laboratory staff had the highest average dose because they were few in number and were involved in nearly all brachytherapy procedures. Ward nurses had lower average annual doses but, because of their larger numbers, contributed the largest fraction of collective dose. A study of Canadian brachytherpy workers found a similar division of

[5]In this Section, occupational exposures are listed for specific radiation therapy procedures. In some cases these exposures reflect the experience of one or a few institutions and may not represent average exposures nationally or exposures consistent with ALARA levels.

collective dose: 66 percent to ward nurses, 11 percent to operating room staff, 7 percent to physicians, 6 percent to source laboratory staff, and the remainder divided among several other categories of workers (Leung, 1983). Approximately 20 percent of monitored nurses showed no detectable yearly dose equivalent, approximately 10 percent received more than 5 mSv/y. The annual collective dose was correlated with the number of brachytherapy procedures performed. The average contribution to the annual collective dose was 0.71 person-mSv per interstitial or intracavitary procedure (Leung, 1983).

The patterns of exposure to nursing personnel at four U.S. hospitals over a three-year period have been analyzed (Cobb et al., 1978). As is shown in Figures 8.1 and 8.2 the annual dose distribution follows a log-normal pattern. However, each hospital had a different mean annual dose due to differing workloads, staffing patterns and policy as to who is monitored. Only a few percent of nurses exceed 5 mSv/y and no yearly dose exceeded 11 mSv/y. Figure 8.3 shows that the collective dose to nurses was correlated, but not linearly correlated, to the number of patients treated per year. The average contribution to annual collective dose, including all hospitals and all years in the study, was between 0.35 and 1.5 person-mSv per patient treatment (Cobb et al., 1978). This is in agreement with the results

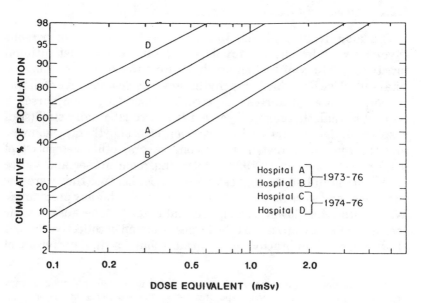

Fig. 8.1 Annual dose equivalent distribution for nursing personnel attending brachytherapy patients averaged over the indicated years. (After Cobb et al., 1978)

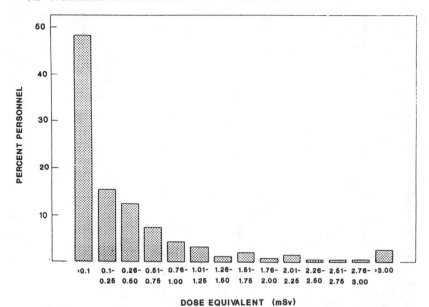

Fig. 8.2 Annual dose distribution for nurses attending brachytherapy patients in all hospitals in the study during the years 1973-1976 (After Cobb *et al.*, 1978).

of Leung, discussed above. The average annual dose per exposed nurse (defined as a nurse having at least one reading in excess of 0.1 mSv) ranged between 0.25 and 1.5 mSv depending on the hospital. From personnel monitoring records Cobb and Svensson determined that the mean annual dose equivalent to radiation therapy personnel in the years 1981 to 1984 was 0.51 mSv for nursing personnel and 1.66 mSv for physicians, residents and implant technologists (Cobb and Svensson, 1985). The best prediction of average annual dose per exposed nurse was the "calculated potential dose" (CPD). The CPD is determined by measuring the dose rate at one meter from each patient, multiplying by the length of time the sources are in place and summing over all patients treated for a given year. The correlation of mean annual dose per exposed nurse with calculated potential dose is shown in Figure 8.4. For any hospital in the study, the mean annual dose per exposed nurse (D/N) is given by the relationship $D/N = 7.0 \times 10^{-4} \times CPD$. In Figure 8.4, the mean annual dose per exposed nurse ranges from approximately 0.3 mSv/y for an institution which treated from 20 to 30 patients per year to approximately 1.4 mSv/y for an institution which treated from 75 to 90 patients per year.

Information of the type summarized above is useful in identifying indicators for initiating the optimization process. Each institution

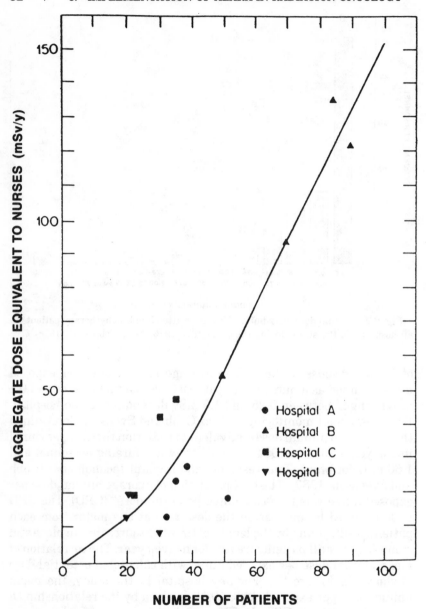

Fig. 8.3 Relationship of the total annual dose equivalent to nurses reported for each hospital to the number of brachytherapy patients treated at that hospital for that year (After Cobb *et al.*, 1978).

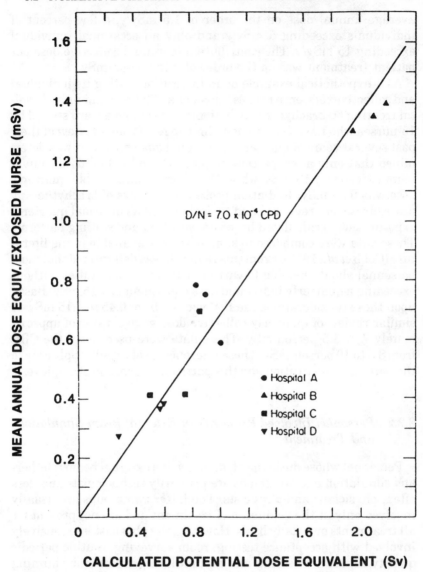

Fig. 8.4 Reported mean annual dose equivalent per exposed nurse as a function of the calculated potential dose (After Cobb *et al.*, 1978).

should review its own facility workload and exposure patterns to validate the analytic approaches reviewed here and perhaps to develop approaches more suitable for the facility. The institutions reviewed here could carry out brachytherapy treatments with an average annual dose on the order of 1.5 mSv/y, a few percent of individuals exceeding 5 mSv/y and only an occasional individual exceeding 15 mSv/y. The contribution to annual collective dose per patient treatment was on the order of 0.75 person-mSv.

As a hypothetical example of an institution setting its individual and collective reference ranges, consider a 450-bed community hospital treating 60 brachytherapy patients per year on a ward staffed by 15 nurses who have been issued film badges. From a review of their past several years of quarterly total film badge records it was determined that only a few percent of quarterly individual dose equivalents exceeded 1.15 mSv while the average measurable quarterly dose was 0.45 mSv. Radiation protection surveys of brachytherapy procedures were reviewed and typical as well as maximal quarterly exposures were calculated based on workload and staffing patterns. These data were compared to similar studies available in the literature (Cobb *et al.*, 1978). From this review it was determined that most personnel should be able to carry out their normal duties without exceeding a quarterly individual dose equivalent of 1.15 mSv. Based upon these considerations the IRR was set from 0.45 to 1.15 mSv. A similar review of quarterly collective dose gave a value of approximately 7 ± 1.5 person-mSv. These data were used to set the CRR from 8.5 to 10 person-mSv. These reference levels would apply only to the particular institution and this particular subgroup of employees.

8.2.2 *Personnel Involved Primarily in External Beam Simulation and Treatment*

Personnel whose duties most often involve external beam teletherapy simulation and treatment are primarily technologists and, less often, physicians and physicists. The latter two groups are usually involved only at the beginning of treatment and are not present for all treatments on a daily basis. However, the physicist is extensively involved with acceptance testing, room surveying, routine periodic quality assurance testing and accumulating treatment planning data. These activities constitute a potential source of exposure for the physicist and support personnel. Simulation and other uses of diagnostic x rays for radiation oncology patients are not a large contributor to the exposure of these personnel. In one study at a large cancer hospital, all of the diagnostic x-ray activities in support of oncology (including all radiological examinations before treatment) contributed only half as much collective dose as treatment activities (Leung, 1983). For a hospital or clinic in which the only source of diagnostic x rays in the oncology section is a simulator, the relative contribution to collective dose would be even less. Hence, the exposure of technologists in the course of daily external beam treatments is usually the most significant circumstance to be considered unless job assignments are so specialized that certain technologists work exclusively in simulation.

Typical exposure patterns for this subcategory of worker depend on the type of teletherapy equipment, facility design and workload. In one study of radiation oncology installations in Great Britain (Hughes *et al.*, 1983) it was reported that the average dose to therapy technologists was approximately 1 mSv/y. Approximately 2 percent exceeded 5 mSv/y and no individual exceeded 15 mSv/y. The personnel in this study operated all types of external beam equipment. The workload in terms of patients per year or treatments per year was not reported. Hoffman and Nath have estimated that exposure to leakage radiation from the source head in the treatment room may result in 1 to 2 mSv/y average dose equivalent to technologists working solely with ^{60}Co teletherapy units (Hoffman and Nath, 1982). The same study noted that technologists working solely with 4 MV and 6 MV linear accelerators never received measurable monthly film badge exposures, but that those working on a 25 MV linear accelerator did receive measurable exposures. The exposure from the high energy linac was due primarily to radioisotopes produced by photoactivation of air and accelerator components. The authors calculated that, for their equipment, the maximum yearly individual dose equivalent was 1 mSv/y for a workload of 32 patients per day, 5 days per week and 50 working weeks per year. The measured average annual exposure to technologists operating both low and high energy linear accelerators was 0.33 mSv/y (Hoffman and Nath, 1982). The dose to technologists from air activation has been calculated by McGinley *et al.* (1984), for a workload of 40 patients per day, five days per week. Their results are shown in Table 8.1 (McGinley *et al.*, 1984). Since activation of materials in the treatment head was not considered, these calculations are consistent with the observa-

TABLE 8.1—*Total dose equivalent to the skin of technologists due to the production of ^{15}O and ^{13}N by air activation.*[a]

Accelerator energy (MeV)	Dose equivalent per year (mSv)
17	0.019
25	0.148
33	0.257
45	0.306

[a]Assumptions are as follows: 40 patients per day, five days per week, given dose of 4 Gy/patient, a treatment time of 120 s and a stay time by the technologist of 600 s per treatment (after McGinley *et al.*, 1984).

tions of Hoffman and Nath. In reviewing the 14-year history of exposure of radiotherapy technicians at the Ontario Cancer Institute, Leung reported an annual average dose of approximately 0.6 mSv/y and an annual collective dose of 70 person-mSv for an annual workload of approximately 75,000 patient treatment visits (Leung 1983). The year-by-year summary, shown in Figure 8.5, includes exposure from all external beam sources including orthovoltage x

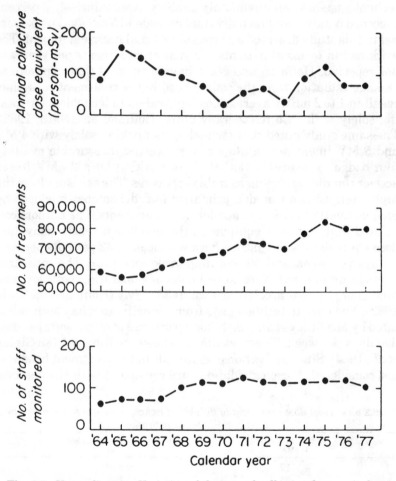

Fig. 8.5 Upper diagram: Variation of the annual collective dose equivalent to hospital staff as a result of the use of external radiation therapy for the period between 1964 and 1977. Middle diagram: Number of treatment visits for external radiation therapy in each of the calendar years. Lower diagram: Number of staff monitored who were exposed to this type of radiation in each of the calendar years. Reproduced from Leung, 1983 with permission.

ray, cobalt-60 and megavoltage x-ray equipment. No individual technologist's dose exceeded 15 mSv in a given year, less than five percent exceed 5 mSv and 75 percent of technologists had no detectable annual exposure. On average, each patient treatment contributed approximately 0.8 person-μSv to the annual collective dose, although the annual collective dose was not highly correlated with workload.

Information of the type summarized above is useful in identifying indicators for initiating the optimization process. Although each institution may be different, it is evident that the institutions reviewed here could carry out external beam therapy (not including brachytherapy) with an average annual dose in the range of 1 mSv/y. Since the average annual dose is highly dependent on the number of personnel monitored, comparisons of annual collective dose per unit workload may be more useful. Unfortunately, only one such value (0.8 person-μSv per patient treatment visit) is available in the literature; hence no "representative" value is known. Until such data become available, retrospective analysis of each institution's own collective dose per unit workload may serve as a starting point.

Consider, for example, a small radiotherapy center with a single 6 MV linear accelerator and five technologists treating 35 patients per day. From a review of their past several years of quarterly total radiation monitoring records it was determined that less than five percent of quarterly individual dose equivalent exceeded 0.8 mSv while the average measurable quarterly dose equivalent was 0.25 mSv. Radiation protection surveys were also reviewed, and typical as well as maximal quarterly exposures were calculated based on workload and staffing patterns. From this review it was determined that, most of the time, personnel should be able to carry out their normal duties without exceeding a quarterly individual dose equivalent of 0.8 mSv. Based upon these considerations the IRR was set from 0.25 to 0.8 mSv. A similar review of quarterly collective dose records, corrected for trends in workload, revealed that the average quarterly collective dose equivalent was approximately 1.25 ± 0.3 person-mSv. These data were used to set the CRR from 1.55 to 1.85 person-mSv. In this case, these reference levels apply only to the subgroup of personnel engaged in simulation and external beam treatment, and would not necessarily be applicable to any other institution or subgroup of employees.

One characteristic of the external beam treatment personnel subgroup is that most often not many institutional options are available to optimize radiation exposure patterns once a facility is in operation. The leakage and photoactivation characteristics of megavoltage teletherapy equipment cannot be modified by individual institutions. Shielding design is obviously important during the construction phase of a facility. It is not usually cost effective to modify wall and ceiling shielding once in place, although it may be cost effective to modify door shielding. Cobalt-60 head leakage and photoactivated radionuclides are not affected by room shielding design. Average exposures from these sources may be affected by modifications of staffing patterns and treatment procedures, but such measures are unlikely to affect collective dose. Hence, once a facility is built and operational, the observed exposure patterns may have to be considered optimal, regardless of their level, because few cost-effective options may be available to modify the exposure patterns.

8.3 Hypothetical Examples of Optimization Decisions in Implementing ALARA

8.3.1 Example of Implementing ALARA for Radiation Oncology Technologists

As an example of the manner in which ALARA might be implemented, consider the following hypothetical situation: A free-standing radiation oncology treatment center is equipped with a ^{60}Co teletherapy unit, an 18 MV linear accelerator which produces 10 MV photons and up to 18 MeV electrons, and a simulator. There is no brachytherapy performed by personnel at this facility. The potentially exposed staff consists of six technologists, a dosimetrist/simulator technologist, a physicist and two physicians. The facility treats approximately 45 to 50 patients per day for a total of about 450 new patients per year. In initiating the ALARA program for the facility, the personnel monitoring records for the past several years were reviewed. A distribution of yearly and quarterly radiation monitor values was plotted and found to be in reasonable agreement with the expected log-normal behavior. The average annual dose equivalent of all monitored employees was 0.55 mSv and the average annual dose equivalent of monitored employees receiving at least one measurable reading during the year was 0.9 mSv. The maximum yearly dose equivalent received by any individual was 3.75 mSv and the average yearly collective dose equivalent was 5.5 person-mSv. From this experience it was decided to base the ALARA program on a review of quarterly totals of radiation monitor readings. The IRR was set from 0.55 to 1 mSv per quarter and the CRR was set from 1.5 to 1.9 person-mSv per quarter.

At a review one technologist was noted to have a quarterly dose of 1.25 mSv, while the collective dose for the quarter was 1.85 person-mSv. Since the IRR was exceeded, the situation was recognized as potentially non-optimum and immediately referred for further assessment. A review of the monthly radiation monitor records for the quarter in question revealed that, of the 1.25 mSv, 0.9 mSv was received in one month. The records of the commercial monitoring service indicated that there were no unusual circumstances, such as light leaks or uneven exposures associated with the 0.9 mSv value. Area radiation monitors and the monitors of other personnel revealed no unusual values. Based on a review of the monitoring data alone there was no reason to doubt the accuracy of the exposure. Treatment records were then reviewed to ascertain whether the reading in question could be due to a temporary increase in workload. In this particular case, the workload was approximately the same as that during the previous several months. The technologist receiving the exposure was then interviewed to see whether personal work habits could have contributed to the exposure. The interview revealed that during the month of greatest exposure the technologist was assigned to the ^{60}Co unit. Furthermore, the other technologist working the unit had suffered a sprained wrist and was unable to assist in positioning blocks in the blocking tray. It was, therefore, concluded that the technologist had most probably received the unusual exposure because more time than usual was spent in the field of ^{60}Co head leakage. Because it was impossible to modify the head leakage characteristics of the unit, the only possible responses were "take no action", "modify procedure" and "modify personnel/ and or training." In this case, it was decided that the optimal response was to take no action. Because technologists normally rotate among machines, and because the sprained wrist was a temporary situation, the individual dose exceeding the IRR was judged to be an acceptable fluctuation. It was unlikely that the elevated exposure would continue. Reassignment of staff duties (*i.e.*, moving the "unusually exposed" staff member to a low exposure position) such that the occupational exposure was more evenly distributed would not reduce collective dose, but would disrupt staffing schedules possibly to the detriment of patient care.

8.3.2 Example of Implementing ALARA for Brachytherapy Nursing

As an additional example of the manner in which an ALARA program might function, consider the following hypothetical example. A 450-bed community hospital treats approximately 60 brachytherapy patients per year on a ward staffed by 15 monitored nurses.

Following a review of their radiation protection history, consultation with nearby institutions and a review of the literature, an ALARA program was instituted based on a quarterly IRR of from 0.45 to 1.15 mSv and a quarterly CRR of from 8.5 to 10 person-mSv. The facility treated gynecological, breast, and head and neck cancer, primarily with afterloaded implants of ^{137}Cs and ^{192}Ir. Patients were always treated in designated rooms at one end of the ward. Only one room adjoined the treatment rooms.

In a quarterly review of personnel monitoring records it was noted that the collective dose was 12 person-mSv, which exceeded the CRR and initiated the optimization procedure. Although the IRR was not exceeded, several individual doses fell within the IRR. Furthermore, a review of past quarters indicated that collective dose was rising while the workload, in terms of type and number of implants, had remained more or less constant. None of the individual radiation monitor values appeared to be due to malfunction or misuse. Interviews with the head nurse and several staff nurses indicated that they attempted to share the patient care duties for implant patients as equally as possible among the designated nurses.

In this case, all possible responses except "take no action" were considered because it was felt that the institution had, in the past, provided the same level of workload and care at a lower collective dose. Thus, the options were to modify shielding, modify procedures or modify personnel and/or training. Nursing care procedures for brachytherapy patients were reviewed, but considered not amenable to significant changes without affecting the quality of patient care. The two remaining options were to increase the level of radiation safety training and awareness on the part of the nursing staff and to purchase additional shielding in the form of portable shields. Two portable shields were considered for purchase at a cost of $3,000 and an expected lifetime of ten years. The portable shields would reduce torso exposure but not head and neck exposure. It was estimated that the portable shields might reduce the effective whole body collective dose by approximately 15 person-mSv per year, although this reduction would not necessarily be reflected in personnel monitoring records, since the film badges were often worn on the collar. The approximate cost of reduction was thus estimated to be $20,000/person-Sv. In reviewing the options with the radiation safety committee a two-step approach was adopted. First, increased effort was put into in-service training of the oncology ward nurses concerning the principles of radiation safety when working with implant patients. Second, it was decided to purchase the portable shields. This was a result of the radiation safety committee's acceptance of the $20,000/person-Sv figure and a result of their belief that the portable shields might have additional subjective value in assuring the staff that every reasonable effort was being expended on their behalf. It should be noted that another institution might consider the purchase of portable shields not to be justified.

9. Implementation of ALARA in Dentistry

9.1 Occupational Exposure in Dentistry

Ionizing radiation is used in dental practice only for radiography. The overwhelming majority of use is for conventional dental radiography. However, use of panoramic radiography is growing and its influence on occupational exposure has not been determined. The only other projection used with significant frequency in current dentistry is the lateral cephalogram.

As with any radiographic installation, the only significant source of occupational exposure in dentistry is scatter from the patient. With modern equipment, tubehead leakage is minimal. A relatively insignificant source of scatter that has received much attention in the dental literature in recent years is the pointer cone, which until recently was used as an aiming device on virtually all conventional dental x-ray machines. Its use placed a thin layer of low-Z material in the beam. Currently, most states require use of an open cylinder as an aiming device; many require that the cylinder be lined with lead to absorb scatter arising from the filter.

9.2 Normative Patterns of Occupational Exposure and Workload, and Indicators for Suspicion of Non-ALARA Situations

As shown in Table 9.1 (EPA, 1984), the number of occupationally-exposed individuals in dentistry has increased dramatically since

TABLE 9.1—*Occupational dose equivalent in dentistry (after EPA, 1984).*

Year	1960	1965	1970	1975	1980	1985[a]
Workers (thousands)	135	150	177	215	259	305
Mean annual dose equivalent (mSv)	1.1	0.8	0.6	0.4	0.2	0.1
Collective dose equivalent (person-Sv)	150	120	100	80	60	30

[a]Estimated

92

1960. However, the mean annual occupational dose equivalent has undergone a greater proportional decrease, so that the collective dose has decreased at a greater rate than that of any other subgroup within medicine and dentistry.

Dentistry accounts for the largest single subgroup of occupationally-exposed individuals in medicine and dentistry. In 1980, the dental work force comprised 44 percent of all potentially exposed persons in medicine and dentistry, and 20 percent of potentially exposed persons of all occupations (EPA, 1984). In comparison, in 1975, dentistry accounted for 49 percent of potentially exposed persons in medicine and dentistry, and 24 percent of all potentially exposed persons of all occupations. Thus, the dental work force has not grown as rapidly as have other segments of the occupationally-exposed population.

All available studies have indicated that virtually all of the collective dose from occupational exposure in dentistry has resulted from exposure of a small segment of dental workers. In 1980, although the mean annual dose equivalent for dentistry was 0.2 mSv, it was 0.7 mSv for those dental workers who received measurable exposure. More than 95 percent of dentists and dental auxiliary personnel received less than 0.1 mSv, the usual threshold of detection in 1980, and more than 98 percent received less than 0.5 mSv (EPA, 1984). A 1976 study found measurable occupational dose equivalent in only 2.5 percent of dental personnel, and estimated the mean annual occupational dose equivalent as less than 0.05 mSv (Crabtree et al., 1976). None of these studies related occupational dose equivalent to workload.

Because dentistry contributes only 15 percent of the collective dose equivalent of medicine and dentistry, and only 3.7 percent of all occupations, and because well over 90 percent of dental personnel receive less than measurable exposures, major changes in dental occupational exposures result in only small changes for medical occupational exposure as a whole. It is tempting to conclude that further occupational exposure reduction in dentistry may not be cost-effective. Conversely, any measurable occupational exposure to dental personnel may be regarded as indicative of a non-ALARA situation, since it appears that more than 90 percent of dental personnel can perform their radiographic duties without incurring measurable exposure. It thus seems reasonable to examine any measurable occupational exposure to dental personnel with the aim of eliminating it. Because of the small exposures involved, however, it may be necessary to limit optimization procedures to those that incur little or no cost and certainly have no adverse effect on patient care.

9.3 Specific Examples of Optimization Decisions in Implementing ALARA

The previously-cited 1976 study found that measurable occupational exposure in dentistry was almost always associated with a breakdown of routine radiation protection, principally the absence of sufficient distance or a barrier between the operator and the x-ray source (Crabtree *et al.*, 1976). Anecdotal evidence also suggests that formal shielding designs are rarely conducted by consultants in dental office design. This suggests that there is potential for improvements in dental radiation protection.

Application of the ALARA principle to radiation protection in dentistry may be illustrated by a hypothetical example. A new dental facility has opened for operation employing four dentists and one dental hygienist as appropriately credentialed operators of x-ray equipment. The hygienist exposed more than 90 percent of the radiographs in the small x-ray cubicle. Because of available historical data from other facilities, the IRR is set from "minimum detectable" to 0.15 mSv per quarter. Data must be accumulated before the CRR can be set. The first quarterly report indicates that the hygienist has received 0.3 mSv. Although small in comparison to exposure typically observed for medical x-ray workers, this exposure is considered significant in comparison to exposures typically observed for dental x-ray workers. Evaluation of the situation finds that there is inadequate space for the hygienist to move to a sufficient distance from the x-ray machine, and no barrier is available. An appropriate shield could have been included in the original construction at trivial cost. However, with aesthetic considerations, addition of such a shield to the facility is estimated to cost some $500. The decision is made to install the shield, although its cost-effectiveness is at best marginal. Another facility might decide not to do so. Psychological factors, such as the response of the exposed individual, may play a role in such decisions.

If all else is equal, operator exposure is directly proportional to patient exposure. Several recent developments provide mechanisms for reducing both, with either beneficial effect or no effect on radiographic image quality, and at little or no cost. These developments may affect the implementation of ALARA.

Most states currently require that diagnostic x-ray beams be collimated to the area of clinical interest or to the size of the image receptor—except for intraoral dental radiography. The conventional intraoral dental film is 3.1 × 4.1 cm but the conventional dental beam is circular, with a diameter of up to 7 cm at skin entry, and perhaps 8 cm in the film plane. The oversize beam has been permitted because the film may be hidden in the patient's mouth, and a larger field minimizes cone cutting. However, beam-film alignment devices which provide for collimation of the beam to the size of the film have been commercially available for some 20 years. Cost is moderate—about $250 total per facility. These devices provide additional benefits, chiefly facilitation of the exposure process and improved image quality. Scatter exposure to the patient is reduced by a factor of about five (Gibbs *et al.*, 1984). Operator exposure should be similarly reduced.

Direct-exposure, non-screen film is the standard for intraoral dental radiography. Currently, virtually all dentists are using film of ANSI speed group D (12 to 24 reciprocal roentgens). In 1981, a new film with very nearly twice the speed (ANSI speed group E-24 to 48 reciprocal roentgens) was introduced by a major manufacturer. Acceptance of the film has been slow, and it accounts for only about 15 percent of dental film sales by its manufacturer.[6] Use of the faster films permits a 40 percent reduction in patient exposure with no change in other technique factors or projection geometry. A similar reduction in operator exposure should be observed. Although there are anecdotal reports of decreased image quality (as judged subjectively) with the new film, receiver operating characteristic (ROC) analysis has demonstrated no difference in lesion detection between the new film and the standard (White *et al.*, 1984a; 1984b). A xerographic imaging system for intraoral use was also introduced (Gratt *et al.*, 1979). This image receptor is approximately the same speed as the new film, and maintains lesion detectability as determined by ROC analysis (Langlais, 1981).

Because the purchase price of speed group D and E films is identical, the cost of dose reduction by changing is zero. A change to xeroradiographic imaging requires an expenditure of a few thousand dollars for the equipment. However, the expenditure is associated with other advantages in addition to dose reduction. A dental practitioner or institution may decide to implement rectangular collimation of intraoral x-ray beams or to convert to a higher-speed image receptor with the major goal of improving patient care. Implementing the ALARA principle may be added to the list of reasons for making such a change.

---

[6]Personal communication from Don Titus, former Director, Dental Trade Relations, Radiography Markets Division, Eastman Kodak Company, Rochester, N.Y.

10. Conclusion

The requirement that all occupational exposures be as low as reasonably achievable is essentially a requirement that professional experience, reasoning and judgement be utilized in the supervision of radiation protection. There are many ways in which reason and judgement may be exercised. Previous sections proferred guidance in the form of a model system based upon awareness, analysis, rational decision making and follow up. A minimum requirement of an ALARA program is an ongoing awareness of the patterns of occupational exposure that goes beyond simple assurance that dose limits are being satisfied. The use of reference levels in conjunction with the routine review of personnel monitoring data offers a method of assuring awareness and focussing effort. Attainment of exposure that is as low as reasonably achievable requires that decisions be made between different levels of radiation protection and different levels of resource expenditure.

Previous sections have emphasized that ALARA decisions should constitute an optimization process, and that one possible method of optimization is cost benefit analysis. The problems inherent in cost-benefit analysis for operational radiation safety in a health care environment place limits on its formal use. Hence, the current importance of cost-benefit analysis is primarily as a conceptual model to guide the decision-making process.

Finally, the implementation and operation of the ALARA concept were illustrated through the use of hypothetical examples. This was done to emphasize the diversity of situations encountered in occupational exposures in medicine and dentistry, to avoid the codification of ALARA into a set of rules and numerical limits, and to encourage institutions to adapt and customize the model system to fit local needs and capabilities.

The maintenance of exposure levels that are as low as reasonably achievable is a challenging and important task. It is essential, however, to adequate radiation protection.

96

APPENDIX A

Glossary

absorbed dose *(D)*: The energy imparted per unit mass by ionizing radiation to matter at a specified point. The SI unit of absorbed dose is joule per kilogram (J/kg). The special name for this unit is gray (Gy). (See Report No. 82, NCRP, 1985b).

activity *(A)*: The number of nuclear transitions occurring in a given quantity of radioactive material per unit time. The SI unit of activity is s^{-1}. The special name for the unit of activity is becquerel (Bq). (See Report No. 82, NCRP, 1985b).

air kerma: See kerma.

ALARA: A principle of radiation protection that encourages management to limit radiation exposures of exposed persons. *As Low As Reasonably Achievable*, economic and social factors being taken into account.

angiography: The radiographic visualization of blood vessels following introduction of contrast material. **cerebral a.**, radiography of the vascular system of the brain after injection of contrast material into the arterial blood stream. **coronary a.**, radiographic visualization of the coronary arteries after the introduction of contrast material. **digital subtraction a.**, radiographic visualization of blood vessels, with images produced by subtracting background structures and enhancing the contrast of those areas that change in density between a preliminary "mask" image and subsequent images.

angioplasty: Reconstruction of blood vessels. **percutaneous transluminal a.**, dilatation of a blood vessel by means of a balloon catheter inserted through the skin and into the chosen vessel and then passed through the lumen of the vessel to the site of the lesion, where the balloon is inflated to flatten plaque against the artery wall.

becquerel (Bq): The special name for the SI unit of activity. One becquerel is one reciprocal second or $1\ s^{-1}$. $3.7 \times 10^{10} Bq = 1\ Ci$.

brachytherapy: Use of an encapsulated source to deliver gamma or beta radiation at a distance up to a few centimeters by surface, intracavitary or interstetial application.

97

cardiac catheterization: Passage of a small catheter through a vein in an arm, leg or neck and into the heart, permitting the securing of blood samples, determination of intracardiac pressure and detection of cardiac anomalies.

cinefluorography: The making of a motion picture record of the successive images appearing on a fluoroscopic screen; called also *cine.*

collective dose equivalent *(S)*: Most frequently the product of the mean dose equivalent for a population and the number of persons in the population, but, more precisely, and preferably, the sum of all individual dose equivalents in the population of concern.

collective reference range (CRR): That range of collective dose equivalent values that, if exceeded, automatically triggers optimization activity.

computed tomography (CT): An imaging procedure that uses multiple x-ray transmission measurements and a computer program to generate tomographic images of the patient.

digital radiography: A diagnostic procedure using an appropriate radiation source and imaging system which collects, processes, stores, recalls and presents image information in a digital rather than analog fashion.

digital subtraction: An image processing procedure used to improve image contrast by subtracting one digitized image from another.

dose equivalent *(H)*: A quantity, defined for radiation protection purposes, that expresses on a common scale for all radiations, the irradiation incurred by exposed persons. It is defined as the product of the absorbed dose *(D)* and the quality factor *(Q)*. The name for the unit of dose equivalent (J Kg^{-1}) is the sievert (Sv).

effective dose equivalent *(H$_E$)*: The sum over specified tissues of the products of the dose equivalent *(H)* in a tissue (T) and the weighting factor for that tissue *(w$_T$)*, i.e., $H_E = \Sigma\ w_T H_T$(NCRP, 1987a). Also $H_E = H_{wb}$ (See whole body dose equivalent).

embolization: Therapeutic introduction of a substance into a vessel in order to occlude it.

exposure: In this report, exposure is used most often in its more general sense and not as the specifically defined radiation quantity. In certain instances "exposure" is used in a formal sense as a measure of the quantity of x or gamma radiation based upon its ability to ionize air through which it passes. The SI unit of *exposure* is coulomb per kilogram.

generator: Device that uses a parent radionuclide to obtain its product, the daughter radionuclide, usually by adding a solution that only interacts with the daughter *(e.g.,* ^{99m}Tc from ^{99}Mo).

gray (Gy): The special name for the SI unit of absorbed dose, kerma, and specific energy imparted. $1 \text{ Gy} = 1 \text{ J Kg}^{-1}$.

image intensifier: An x-ray image receptor which increases the brightness of a fluoroscopic image by electronic amplification and image minification.

image receptor: A system for deriving a diagnostically usable image from the x rays transmitted through the patient. Examples: screen-film system; stimulable phosphor; solid state detector.

individual reference range (IRR): That range of individual dose equivalent values that, if exceeded, automatically triggers optimization activity.

interventional radiology: Diagnostic and therapeutic radiologic techniques that entail manipulation within the body after introduction of a catheter or other instrument through a natural opening or through the skin.

kerma: The sum of the initial kinetic energies of all the charged ionizing particles liberated by uncharged ionizing particles per unit mass of a specified material. Kerma is measured in the same unit as absorbed dose. The SI unit of kerma is joule per kilogram and its special name is gray (Gy). Kerma can be quoted for any specified material at a point in free space or in an absorbing medium.

MDL (minimum detectable level): The threshold of detection for the device in question.

monitor, personnel: See personnel monitor.

negligible individual risk level (NIRL): A level of risk that can be dismissed, nominally an annual risk of 10^{-7} (NCRP, 1987a). This risk is that associated with an annual effective dose equivalent of 0.01 mSv.

occupational exposure: The exposure of an individal to ionizing radiation in the course of employment in which the individuals normal duties or authorized activities necessarily involve the likelihood of exposure to ionizing radiation.

optimal radiation protection: In this report, that level of radiation protection that, when either increased or decreased, results in decreased net benefit. Hence optimal radiation protection yields the greatest net benefit to society.

optimization of radiation protection: The process of determining and providing optimal radiation protection. This has the same meaning as ALARA.

organ weighting factor (w_T): A factor that indicates the ratio of the risk of stochastic effects attributable to irradiation of a given organ or tissue (T) to the total risk when the whole body is uniformly irradiated.

personnel dosimeters: Devices designed to be worn or carried by an individual for the purpose of determining the dose equivalent received *(e.g.,* film badges, pocket chambers, pocket dosimeters, ring badges, thermoluminescent dosimeters, etc.).

personnel monitor: Also known as personal monitor. An appropriately sensitive device used to estimate the absorbed dose or effective dose equivalent received by an individual.

potentially exposed: In this report, all monitored and unmonitored personnel who have the potential for being exposed to radiation in the course of their duties.

protective apron: An apron made of radiation absorbing materials, used to reduce radiation exposure.

protective barrier: A barrier of radiation absorbing material(s) used to reduce radiation exposure.

primary protective barrier: A protective barrier used to attenuate the useful beam for radiation protection purposes.

secondary protective barrier: A barrier sufficient to attenuate stray radiation (scattered plus leakage) for radiation protection purposes.

radiation (ionizing): Any electromagnetic or particulate radiation capable of producing ions, directly or indirectly, by interaction with matter. Examples are x-ray photons, charged atomic particles and other ions, and neutrons.

leakage radiation: All radiation coming from within the source assembly except for the useful beam. (Note: Leakage radiation includes the portion of the radiation coming directly from the source and not absorbed by the source assembly, as well as the scattered radiation produced within the source assembly).

scattered radiation: Radiation that, during passage through matter is changed in direction. (The change is usually accompanied by a decrease in energy).

radiation protection survey: An evaluation of the radiation safety in and around an installation, that includes radiation measurements, inspections, evaluations and recommendations.

radiation receptor: Any device that absorbs a portion of the incident radiation energy and converts this portion into another form of energy which can be more easily used to produce desired results *(e.g.,* production of an image). See image receptor.

radiograph: A film or other record produced by the action of x rays on a sensitized surface.

radiography: The production of images on film or other record by the action of x rays transmitted through the patient.

radiopharmaceutical: A radioactive pharmaceutical or chemical used for diagnostic or therapeutic purposes.

radiopharmacy: The preparation of radioactive pharmaceuticals and radionuclides. Also, the place at which radiopharmaceuticals are prepared.

reference level: The predetermined value of a quantity, below a limit, which triggers a specified course of action when the value, usually a dose level, is exceeded or is expected to be exceeded. (See NCRP Report No. 91, 1987a).

scattered radiation: See radiation.

secondary protective barrier: See protective barrier.

sealed source: A radioactive source sealed in a container or having a bonded cover, in which the container or cover has sufficient mechanical strength to prevent contact with and dispersion of the radioactive material under the conditions of use for which it was designed.

sievert (Sv): The special name for the SI unit of dose equivalent. One sievert equals one joule per kilogram.

spot film: A radiograph taken during a fluoroscopic examination for the purpose of providing a permanent record of an area of interest or to verify the filling of a void with contrast media.

stochastic effects: Effects, the probability of which, rather than their severity, is a function of radiation dose without threshold. (More generally, stochastic means random in nature).

teletherapy: Treatment in which the source of radiation is at a distance from the body, as contrasted to brachytherapy.

tomography: A special technique to show in detail images of structures lying in a predetermined plane of tissue, while blurring or eliminating detail in images of structures in other planes.

whole body dose equivalent (H_{wb}): The dose equivalent associated with the uniform irradiation of the whole body.

workload (W): The degree of use of a radiation source. For x-ray machines operating at tube potentials below 500 kV, the workload is usually expressed in milliampere minutes per week. For gamma-beam therapy sources and for photon-emitting equipment operating at 500 kV or above, the workload is usually stated in terms of the weekly kerma of the useful beam at one meter from the source and is expressed in grays per week at one meter.

References

AHA (1984). American Hospital Association. *Hospital Statistics* (American Hospital Association, Chicago).

AHLUWALIA, B., ALLEN, E.W., BASMADJIAN, G. AND ICE, R. (1981). "The role of nuclear pharmacy in reducing radiation exposure," Health Phys. **40**, 728–729.

ANGER, R.T. (1977). "Radiation protection in nuclear medicine," American Association of Physicists in Medicine Summer School on The Physics of Clinical Nuclear Medicine, University of Kentucky, Lexington, Kentucky.

AUXIER, J. AND DICKSON, H. (1983). "Guest Editorial: Concern over recent use of the ALARA philosophy," Health Phys. **44**, 595.

BALTER, S., SONES, F.M., AND BRANCATO, L. (1978). "Radiation exposure to the operator performing cardiac angiography with U-arm systems," Circulation **58**, 925–932.

BARRALL, R. AND SMITH, I. (1976). "Personnel radiation exposure and protection from Tc-99m radiations," in *Biophysical Aspects of the Medical Use of Technetium-99m*, AAPM Monograph No. 1, Kereiakes, J.G and Corey, K. R., Eds., (American Institute of Physics, New York).

BARRALL, R.C., LANZL, L.H. AND HILBERT, J.H. (1978). "A survey of personnel exposure in nuclear medicine," Med. Phys. **5**, 568.

BRAHMAVAR, S.M., LAFRANCE, M., TIDWELL, A. AND VANDERLICK, C. (1984). "Personnel exposures in x-ray special procedures and in radionuclide therapy: a five year study," Baystate Medical Center, Springfield, Massachusetts. Personal Communication.

BRANSON, B.M., SODD, V.J., NISHIYAMA, H., AND WILLIAMS, C.C. (1976). "Use of syringe shields in clinical practice," J. Clin. Med. **1**, 56.

BRANSON, B.M., SODD, V.J., WILLIAMS, C.C., NISHIYAMA, H., VAN TUINEN, R.J., AND KRUGER, J. (1977). "Selection criteria for syringe shields," Proceedings of the 18th Annual Meeting of the Southeastern Chapter of the Society of Nuclear Medicine, Winston-Salem, North Carolina.

BRATEMAN, L., BOWERS, W.G., DUNNICK, N.R. AND DOPPMAN, J.L. (1979). "Transparent protective barrier for fluoroscopy during angiography," Amer. J. Roentgenol. **133**, 954–955.

BRATEMAN, L., SHAWKER, T.H., AND CONCA, D.M. (1980). "Potential hazard to ultrasonographers from previously administered radionuclides," Radiology **134**, 479–482.

BURKS, J., GRIFFITH, P., McCORMICK, K. AND MILLER, R. (1982). "Radiation exposure to nursing personnel from patients receiving diagnostic radionuclides," Heart Lung **11**(3), 217.

BUSH, W.H., BRANNEN, G.E., GIBBONS, R.P., CORREA, R.J. AND ELDER, J.S. (1984). "Radiation exposure to the patient and urologist during percutaneous nephrostolithotomy," J. Urol. **132**, 1148–1152.

BUSH, W.H., JONES, D. AND BRANNEN, G.E. (1985). "Radiation dose to personnel during percutaneous renal calculus removal," Amer. J. Roentgenol. **145**, 1261–1264.

BUSHONG, S.C. (1989). "Personnel monitoring in diagnostic radiology: Revisited—Again! Health Phys. **56**, 565–566 (Correspondence).

COBB, P.D. AND SVENSSON, G.K. (1985). "Radiation exposure and risk assessment from radiation therapy procedures," Oral presentation at 27th meeting of American Association of Physicists in Medicine (American Association of Physicists in Medicine, New York).

COBB, P.D., KASE, K.R. AND BJARNGARD, B.E. (1978). "Radiation exposure of nursing personnel to brachytherapy patients," Health Phys. **34**, 661–665.

CRABTREE, C.L., JOHNSON, O.N., AND GIBBS, S.J. (1976). *Nashville Dental Project: An Educational Approach to Voluntary Improvement of Radiographic Practice.* USHDEW Publication (FDA) 76–8011. (National Technical Information Service, Springfield, Virginia).

DASH, H. AND LEAMAN, D.M. (1984). "Operator radiation exposure during percutaneous transluminal coronary angioplasty," J. Amer. Coll. Cardiology **4**, 725–728.

EPA (1980). Environmental Protection Agency. *Occupational Exposure to Ionizing Radiation in the United States: A Comprehensive Summary for the Year 1975* by Cook, J. R. and Nelson, D. R., EPA 520/4-80-001 (National Technical Information Service, Springfield, Virginia).

EPA (1984). Environmental Protection Agency. *Occupational Exposure to Ionizing Radiation in the United States: A Comprehensive Review for the Year 1980 and a Summary of Trends for the Years 1960–1985* by Kumazawa, S., Nelson, D. R., and Richardson, A. C. EPA 520/1-84-005 (National Technical Information Service, Springfield, Virginia).

FAULKNER, K. AND HARRISON, R.M. (1988). "Estimation of effective dose equivalent to staff in diagnostic radiology," Phys. Med. Biol. **33**, 83–91.

GANDSMAN, E., NORTH, D. AND SPARAGEN, S.C. (1980). "Radiation safety in a nuclear medicine department," Health Phys. **38**, 399–407.

GANDSMAN, E., NORTH, D. AND TYSON, I. (1984). "Update of radiation safety in a nuclear medicine department," Health Phys. **46**, 1293–1295.

GERTZ, E.W., WISNESKI, J.A., GOULD, R.G. AND AKIN, J.R. (1982). "Improved radiation protection for physicians performing cardiac catheterization," Am. J. Cardiol. **50**, 1283–1286.

GIBBS, S.J., PUJOL, A., CHEN, T.S., MALCOLM, A.W., AND JAMES, A.E., Jr. (1984). "Patient risk from interproximal radiography." Oral Surg. **58**, 347–354.

GRATT, B.M., WHITE, S.C., SICKLES, E.A., AND JEROMIN, L.S. (1979). "Imaging properties of intraoral dental xeroradiography." J. Amer. Dent. Assoc. **99**, 805–809.

GUSTAFSSON, M. AND LUNDERQUIST, A. (1981). "Personnel exposure to radiation at some angiographic procedures," Radiology, **140**, 807–811.

HERMAN, M.W., PATRICK, J. AND TABRISKEY, J. (1980). "A Comparative study of scattered radiation levels from 80-kVp and 240-kVp x-rays in the surgical intensive care unit," Radiology **137**, (Technical Notes) 552–553.

HOFFMAN, R.J. AND NATH, R. (1982). "On the sources of radiation exposure of technologists in a radiotherapy center with high energy x-ray accelerators," Health Phys. **42**, 525–526.

HUGHES, J.S., ROBERTS, G.C. AND STEPHENSON, S. K. (1983). "Occupational exposure in medicine: a review of radiation doses to hospital staff in northwest England," Br. J. Radiol. **56**, 729–735.

ICRP (1959). International Commission on Radiological Protection. *Recommendations of the ICRP*, ICRP Publication No. 1 (Pergamon Press, New York).

ICRP (1977). International Commission on Radiological Protection. *Recommendations of the ICRP*, ICRP Publication No. 26 (Pergamon Press, New York).

ICRP (1982). International Commission on Radiological Protection. *Protection of the Patient in Diagnostic Radiology*, ICRP Publication No. 34 (Pergamon Press, New York).

ICRP (1983). International Commission on Radiological Protection. *Cost-Benefit Analysis in the Optimization of Radiation Protection*, ICRP Publication No. 37, (Pergamon Press, New York).

ICRP (1985). International Commission on Radiological Protection. *Protection of the Patient in Radiation Therapy*, ICRP Publication No. 44 (Pergamon Press, New York).

ICRP (1987). International Commission on Radiological Protection. *Protection of the Patient in Nuclear Medicine*, ICRP Publication No. 52 (Pergamon Press, New York).

ICRU (1980). International Commission on Radiation Units and Measurements. *Radiation Quantities and Units*, ICRU Report 33 (International Commission on Radiation Units and Measurements, Bethesda, Maryland).

ICRU (1985). International Commission on Radiation Units and Measurements. *Determination of Dose Equivalents Resulting from External Radiation Sources*, ICRU Report 39 (International Commission on Radiation Units and Measurements, Bethesda, Maryland).

ICRU (1988). International Commission on Radiation Units and Measurements. *Detemination of Dose Equivalents from External Radiation Sources—Part 2*, ICRU Report 43 (International Commission on Radiation Units and Measurements, Bethesda, Maryland).

IYER, P.S. AND DHOND, R.V. (1980). "Use of generator-produced radionuclides in nuclear medicine procedures: Analysis of personnel dose and laboratory work practices," Health Phys. **39**, 576–578.

JACOBSON, A. AND KELLY, M.S. (1986). "Practical quantitation of radiation levels associated with newer CT scanner units," Health Phys. **50**, 203–207.

JEANS, S.P., FAULKNER, K., LOVE, H.G. AND BARDSLEY, R.A. (1985). "An investigation of the radiation dose to staff during cardiac radiological studies," Br. J. Radiol. **58**, 419–428.

JOHNSON, J.L. AND ABERNATHY, D.L. (1983). "Diagnostic imaging procedure volume in the United States," Radiology, **146**, 851–853.

KACZMAREK, R.G., BEDNAREK, D.R., WONG, R., RUDIN, S. AND ALKER, G. (1986). "Potential radiation hazards to personnel during dynamic CT," Radiology **161**, 853.

KOSNIK, L.T. AND MEENGS, W.L. (1986). "Personel exposure in the cardiac catheterization laboratory," Health Phys. **50**, 144–147.

KRAMER, S., HANKS, G.E. AND DIAMOND, J.J. (1983). "Summary results from the fourth facilities master list surveys conducted by the patterns of care study. " Int. J. Rad. Onc. Biol. Phys. 9, 1881–1883.

LANGLAIS, R.P., Ed. (1981). *Safe Effective X-ray Workshop Manual* (American Dental Association, Chicago).

LA RIVIERE, P.D. (1985). "Radiotherapy technologist dose from high energy electron medical accelerators," Health Phys. 49, 1105–1114.

LEUNG, P.M.K. (1983). "Personnel radiation exposure analysis in a radiotherapy center: fourteen year retrospective study," Int. J. Rad. Oncol. Biol. Phys. 9, 1705–1713.

MCGINLEY, P.H., WRIGHT, B.A. AND MEDING, C.J. (1984). "Dose to radiotherapy technologists from air activation," Med. Phys. 11, 855–858.

MCGUIRE, E.L., BAKER, M.L. AND VANDERGRIFT, J. (1983). "Evaluation of radiation exposures to personnel in fluoroscopic x-ray facilities," Health Phys. 45, 975–980.

MEINHOLD, C. B. (1989). "Use of effective dose equivalent for external radiation exposures," Health Phys. 56, 570.

MILLER, M.E., DAVIS, M.L., MACCLEAN, C.R., DAVIS, J.G., SMITH, B.L. AND HUMPHRIES, J.R. (1983). "Radiation exposure and associated risks to operating room personnel during use of fluroroscopy: Guidance for selected orthopedic surgical procedures," J. Bone Joint Surg. 64, 1–4.

NAS/NRC (1980). National Academy of Sciences/National Research Council. *The Effects on Populations of Exposure to Low Levels of Ionizing Radiation: 1980*, Committee on the Biological Effects of Ionizing Radiations (BEIR III) (National Academy Press, Washington).

NCRP (1954). National Committee on Radiation Protection. *Permissible Dose from External Sources of Ionizing Radiation*, NCRP Report No. 17, published as National Bureau of Standards Handbook 59, Washington, D. C. (Superseded by NCRP Report No. 39).

NCRP (1971). National Council on Radiation Protection and Measurements. *Basic Radiation Protection Criteria*, NCRP Report No. 39 (National Council on Radiation Protection and Measurements, Bethesda, Maryland) (Superseded by NCRP Report No. 91).

NCRP (1975). National Council on Radiation Protection and Measurements. *Review of the Current State of Radiation Protection Philosophy*, NCRP Report No. 43 (National Council on Radiation Protection and Measurements, Bethesda, Maryland) (Superseded by NCRP Report No. 91).

NCRP (1976). National Council on Radiation Protection and Measurements. *Shielding Design and Evaluation for Medical Use of X-rays and Gamma Rays of Energies Up to 10 MeV*, Report No. 49 (National Council on Radiation Protection and Measurements, Bethesda, Maryland).

NCRP (1978). National Council on Radiation Protection and Measurements. *Operational Radiation Safety Program*, NCRP Report No. 59 (National Council on Radiation Protection, Bethesda, Maryland).

NCRP (1983). National Council on Radiation Protection and Measurements. *Operational Radiation Safety—Training*, NCRP Report No. 71 (National Council on Radiation Protection and Measurements, Bethesda, Maryland).

NCRP (1984). National Council on Radiation Protection and Measurements. *Neutron Contamination from Medical Electron Accelerators*, NCRP Report No. 79 (National Council on Radiation Protection and Measurements, Bethesda, Maryland).

NCRP (1985). National Council on Radiation Protection and Measurements. *SI Units in Radiation Protection and Measurements*, NCRP Report No. 82 (National Council on Radiation Protection and Measurements, Bethesda, Maryland).

NCRP (1986). National Council on Radiation Protection and Measurements. *Mammography—A User's Guide*, NCRP Report No. 85 (National Council on Radiation Protection and Measurements, Bethesda, Maryland).

NCRP (1987a). National Council on Radiation Protection and Measurements. *Recommendations on Limits for Exposure to Ionizing Radiation*, NCRP Report No. 91 (National Council on Radiation Protection and Measurements, Bethesda, Maryland).

NCRP (1987b). National Council on Radiation Protection and Measurements. *Radiation Alarms and Access Control Systems*, NCRP Report No. 88 (National Council on Radiation Protection and Measurements, Bethesda, Maryland).

NCRP (1989a). National Council on Radiation Protection and Measurements. *Exposure of the U. S. Population From Occupational Radiation*, NCRP Report No. 101 (National Council on Radiation Protection and Measurements, Bethesda, Maryland).

NCRP (1989b). National Council on Radiation Protection and Measurements. *Exposure of the U. S. Population from Diagnostic Medical Radiation*, NCRP Report No. 100 (National Council on Radiation Protection and Measurements, Bethesda, Maryland).

NCRP (1991). National Council on Radiation Protection and Measurements. "The assessment of risk for radiation protection purposes" (In preparation).

NISHIYAMA, H. AND LUKES, S.J. (1982). "Exposure to xenon-133 in the nuclear medicine laboratory," Radiology 143, 243–247.

NISHIYAMA, H., LUKES, G. JR., FELLER, P.A., VAN TUINEN, R.J. AND SAENGER, E.L. (1980a). "Survey of ^{99m}Tc contamination of laboratory personnel: Its degree and routes," Radiology 135, 467–471.

NISHIYAMA, H., VAN TUINEN, R.J., LUKES, S.J. AND FELLER, P.A. (1980b). "Survey of ^{99m}Tc contamination of laboratory personnel: hand decontamination," Radiology 137, 549–551.

NISHIYAMA, H., LUKES, S.J., MAYFIELD, G. AND GROSSMAN, L.W. (1980c). "Internal contamination of laboratory personnel by ^{131}I," Radiology 137, 767–771.

NORTH, D. (1985). "Pattern of scattered exposure from portable radiographs" Health Phys. 49 (Notes) 92–93.

RILEY, R.C., BIRKS, J.W., PALACIOS, E. AND TEMPLETON, A.W. (1972). "Exposure of radiologists during special procedures," Radiology, 104, 679–683.

SANTEN, B.C., KAN, K., VELTHUYSE, H.J.M. AND JULIUS, H.W. (1975). "Exposure of the radiologist to scattered radiation during angiography," Radiology 115, 447–450.

SYED, I.B., FLOWERS, N., GRANLICK, D. AND SAMOLS, E. (1982). "Radiation exposure in nuclear cardiovascular studies," Health Phys. **42**, 159–163.

UNSCEAR (1982). United Nations Scientific Committee on the Effects of Atomic Radiation. *Ionizing Radiation Sources and Biological Effects* (United Nations, New York).

UNSCEAR (1988). United Nations Scientific Committee on the Effects of Atomic Radiation. *Sources, Effects and Risks of Ionizing Radiation* (United Nations, New York).

WEBSTER, E.W. (1989). "EDE for exposure with protective aprons," Health Phys. **56**, 568–569 (Correspondence).

WHITE, S.C., HOLLENDER, L. AND GRATT, B.M. (1984a). "Comparison of xeroradiographs and film for detection of proximal surface caries," J. Amer. Dent. Assoc. **108**, 755–759.

WHITE, S.C., HOLLENDER, L. AND GRATT, B.M. (1984b). "Comparison of xeroradiographs and film for detection of periapical lesions," J. Dent. Res. **63**, 910–913.

WOHNI, T. AND STRANDEN, E. (1979). "The new ICRP concept of person-dose related to the film-badge exposure for some geometries and radiation qualities used in medical x-ray" Health Phys. **36**, (notes) 71–73.

The NCRP

The National Council on Radiation Protection and Measurements is a nonprofit corporation chartered by Congress in 1964 to:

1. Collect, analyze, develop, and disseminate in the public interest information and recommendations about (a) protection against radiation and (b) radiation measurements, quantities, and units, particularly those concerned with radiation protection;
2. Provide a means by which organizations concerned with the scientific and related aspects of radiation protection and of radiation quantities, units, and measurements may cooperate for effective utilization of their combined resources, and to stimulate the work of such organizations;
3. Develop basic concepts about radiation quantities, units, and measurements, about the application of these concepts, and about radiation protection;
4. Cooperate with the International Commission on Radiological Protection, the International Commission on Radiation Units and Measurements, and other national and international organizations, governmental and private, concerned with radiation quantities, units, and measurements and with radiation protection.

The Council is the successor to the unincorporated association of scientists known as the National Committee on Radiation Protection and Measurements and was formed to carry on the work begun by the Committee.

The Council is made up of the members and the participants who serve on the over sixty scientific committees of the Council. The scientific committees, composed of experts having detailed knowledge and competence in the particular area of the committee's interest draft proposed recommendations. These are then submitted to the full membership of the Council for careful review and approval before being published.

The following comprise the current officers and membership of the Council:

Officers

President	WARREN K. SINCLAIR
President Elect	CHARLES B. MEINHOLD
Vice President	S. JAMES ADELSTEIN
Secretary and Treasurer	W. ROGER NEY
Assistant Secretary	CARL D. HOBELMAN
Assistant Treasurer	JAMES F. BERG

108

Members

SEYMOUR ABRAHAMSON
S. JAMES ADELSTEIN
PETER R. ALMOND
EDWARD L. ALPEN
LYNN R. ANSPAUGH
JOHN A. AUXIER
WILLIAM J. BAIR
MICHAEL A. BENDER
B. GORDON BLAYLOCK
BRUCE B. BOECKER
JOHN D. BOICE, JR.
ROBERT L. BRENT
ANTONE BROOKS
PAUL L. CARSON
MELVIN W. CARTER
RANDALL S. CASWELL
JAMES E. CLEAVER
FRED T. CROSS
STANLEY B. CURTIS
GERALD D. DODD
PATRICIA W. DURBIN
CARL H. DURNEY
KEITH F. ECKERMAN
CHARLES EISENHAUER
THOMAS S. ELY

JACOB I. FABRIKANT
R. J. MICHAEL FRY
THOMAS F. GESELL
ETHEL S. GILBERT
ROBERT A. GOEPP
JOEL E. GRAY
ARTHUR W. GUY
ERIC J. HALL
NAOMI H. HARLEY
WILLIAM R. HENDEE
DONALD G. JACOBS
A. EVERETTE JAMES, JR.
BERND KAHN
KENNETH R. KASE
HAROLD L. KUNDEL
CHARLES E. LAND
RAY D. LLOYD
HARRY R. MAXON
ROGER O. MCCLELLAN
BARBARA J. MCNEIL
CHARLES B. MEINHOLD
MORTIMER L. MENDELSOHN
FRED A. METTLER
WILLIAM A. MILLS
DADE W. MOELLER

A. ALAN MOGHISSI
JOHN W. POSTON
ANDREW K. POZNANSKI
NORMAN C. RASMUSSEN
CHESTER R. RICHMOND
GENEVIEVE S. ROESSLER
MARVIN ROSENSTEIN
LAWRENCE N. ROTHENBERG
LEONARD A. SAGAN
KEITH J. SCHIAGER
ROBERT A. SCHLENKER
ROY E. SHORE
WARREN K. SINCLAIR
PAUL SLOVIC
RICHARD A. TELL
WILLIAM L. TEMPLETON
THOMAS S. TENFORDE
J. W. THIESSEN
RALPH H. THOMAS
JOHN E. TILL
ROBERT L. ULLRICH
ARTHUR C. UPTON
GEORGE L. VOELZ
GEORGE M. WILKENING
MARVIN ZISKIN

Honorary Members

LAURISTON S. TAYLOR, Honorary President

VICTOR P. BOND
REYNOLD F. BROWN
AUSTIN M. BRUES
GEORGE W. CASARETT
FREDERICK P. COWAN
JAMES F. CROW
MERRILL EISENBUD
ROBLEY D. EVANS
RICHARD F. FOSTER
HYMER L. FRIEDELL
ROBERT O. GORSON

JOHN H. HARLEY
JOHN W. HEALY
LOUIS H.
    HEMPELMANN, JR.
PAUL C. HODGES
GEORGE V. LEROY
WILFRID B. MANN
KARL Z. MORGAN
ROBERT J. NELSEN
WESLEY L. NYBORG

HARALD H. ROSSI
WILLIAM L. RUSSELL
JOHN H. RUST
EUGENE L. SAENGER
WILLIAM J. SCHULL
J. NEWELL STANNARD
JOHN B. STORER
ROY C. THOMPSON
EDWARD W. WEBSTER
HAROLD O. WYCKOFF

Currently, the following subgroups are actively engaged in formulating recommendations:

SC 1   Basic Radiation Protection Criteria
        SC 1-1 Probability of Causation for Genetic and Developmental
            Effects
        SC 1-2 The Assessment of Risk for Radiation Protection Purposes
        SC 1-3 Collective Dose
SC 16   X-Ray Protection in Dental Offices

SC 84-2 Contaminated Soil
SC 85   Risk of Lung Cancer from Radon
SC 86   Hot Particles in Eye, Ear and Lung

Ad Hoc Committee on Comparison of Radiation Exposures
Ad Hoc Group on Nuclear Medicine Misadministration
Ad Hoc Group on Plutonium
Ad Hoc Group on Radon
Ad Hoc Group on Video Display Terminals
Study Group on Comparative Risk
Task Force on Occupational Exposure Levels

In recognition of its responsibility to facilitate and stimulate cooperation among organizations concerned with the scientific and related aspects of radiation protection and measurement, the Council
has created a category of NCRP Collaborating Organizations. Organizations or groups of organizations that are national or international in scope and are concerned with scientific problems involving
radiation quantities, units, measurements, and effects, or radiation
protection may be admitted to collaborating status by the Council.
The present Collaborating Organizations with which the NCRP
maintains liaison are as follows:

American Academy of Dermatology
American Association of Physicists in Medicine
American College of Medical Physics
American College of Nuclear Physicians
American College of Radiology
American Dental Association
American Industrial Hygiene Association
American Institute of Ultrasound in Medicine
American Insurance Services Group
American Medical Association
American Nuclear Society
American Occupational Medical Association
American Podiatric Medical Association
American Public Health Association
American Radium Society
American Roentgen Ray Society
American Society of Radiologic Technologists
American Society for Therapeutic Radiology and Oncology
Association of University Radiologists
Bioelectromagnetics Society
College of American Pathologists
Conference of Radiation Control Program Directors
Electric Power Research Institute
Federal Communications Commission
Federal Emergency Management Agency
Genetics Society of America
Health Physics Society
Institute of Nuclear Power Operations

National Electrical Manufacturers Association
National Institute of Standards and Technology
Nuclear Management and Resources Council
Radiation Research Society
Radiological Society of North America
Society of Nuclear Medicine
United States Air Force
United States Army
United States Department of Energy
United States Department of Housing and Urban Development
United States Department of Labor
United States Environmental Protection Agency
United States Navy
United States Nuclear Regulatory Commission
United States Public Health Service

The NCRP has found its relationships with these organizations to be extremely valuable to continued progress in its program.

Another aspect of the cooperative efforts of the NCRP relates to the special liaison relationships established with various governmental organizations that have an interest in radiation protection and measurements. This liaison relationship provides: (1) an opportunity for participating organizations to designate an individual to provide liaison between the organization and the NCRP; (2) that the individual designated will receive copies of draft NCRP reports (at the time that these are submitted to the members of the Council) with an invitation to comment, but not vote; and (3) that new NCRP efforts might be discussed with liaison individuals as appropriate, so that they might have an opportunity to make suggestions on new studies and related matters. The following organizations participate in the special liaison program:

Australian Radiation Laboratory
Commissariat a l'Energie Atomique (France)
Commission of the European Communities
Defense Nuclear Agency
Federal Emergency Management Agency
Japan Radiation Council
National Institute of Standards and Technology
National Radiological Protection Board (United Kingdom)
National Research Council (Canada)
Office of Science and Technology Policy
Office of Technology Assessment
Ultrasonics Institute of Australia
United States Air Force
United States Army
United States Coast Guard
United States Department of Energy
United States Department of Health and Human Services
United States Department of Labor

United States Department of Transportation
United States Environmental Protection Agency
United States Navy
United States Nuclear Regulatory Commission

The NCRP values highly the participation of these organizations in the liaison program.

The Council's activities are made possible by the voluntary contribution of time and effort by its members and participants and the generous support of the following organizations:

Alfred P. Sloan Foundation
Alliance of American Insurers
American Academy of Dental Radiology
American Academy of Dermatology
American Association of Physicists in Medicine
American College of Medical Physics
American College of Nuclear Physicians
American College of Radiology
American College of Radiology Foundation
American Dental Association
American Hospital Radiology Administrators
American Industrial Hygiene Association
American Insurance Services Group
American Medical Association
American Nuclear Society
American Occupational Medical Association
American Osteopathic College of Radiology
American Podiatric Medical Association
American Public Health Association
American Radium Society
American Roentgen Ray Society
American Society of Radiologic Technologists
American Society for Therapeutic Radiology and Oncology
American Veterinary Medical Association
American Veterinary Radiology Society
Association of University Radiologists
Battelle Memorial Institute
Center for Devices and Radiological Health
College of American Pathologists
Committee on Radiation Research and Policy Coordination
Commonwealth of Pennsylvania
Defense Nuclear Agency
Eastman Kodak Company
Edison Electric Institute
Edward Mallinckrodt, Jr. Foundation
EG&G Idaho, Inc.
Electric Power Research Institute
Federal Emergency Management Agency
Florida Institute of Phosphate Research
Genetics Society of America
Health Effects Research Foundation (Kyoto)

Health Physics Society
Institute of Nuclear Power Operations
James Picker Foundation
Martin Marietta Corporation
National Aeronautics and Space Administration
National Association of Photographic Manufacturers
National Cancer Institute
National Electrical Manufacturers Association
National Institute of Standards and Technology
Nuclear Management and Resources Council
Radiation Research Society
Radiological Society of North America
Richard Lounsbery Foundation
Sandia National Laboratory
Society of Nuclear Medicine
United States Department of Energy
United States Department of Labor
United States Environmental Protection Agency
United States Navy
United States Nuclear Regulatory Commission
Victoreen, Incorporated

To all of these organizations the Council expresses its profound appreciation for their support.

Initial funds for publication of NCRP reports were provided by a grant from the James Picker Foundation and for this the Council wishes to express its deep appreciation.

The NCRP seeks to promulgate information and recommendations based on leading scientific judgment on matters of radiation protection and measurement and to foster cooperation among organizations concerned with these matters. These efforts are intended to serve the public interest and the Council welcomes comments and suggestions on its reports or activities from those interested in its work.

NCRP Publications

NCRP publications are distributed by the NCRP Publications' office. Information on prices and how to order may be obtained by directing an inquiry to:

> NCRP Publications
> 7910 Woodmont Ave., Suite 800
> Bethesda, Md 20814

The currently available publications are listed below.

Proceedings of the Annual Meeting

No.   Title

1   *Perceptions of Risk,* Proceedings of the Fifteenth Annual Meeting, Held on March 14–15, 1979 (Including Taylor Lecture No. 3) (1980)

2   *Quantitative Risk in Standards Setting,* Proceedings of the Sixteenth Annual Meeting, Held on April 2–3, 1980 (Including Taylor Lecture No. 4) (1981)

3   *Critical Issues in Setting Radiation Dose Limits,* Proceedings of the Seventeenth Annual Meeting, Held on April 8–9, 1981 (Including Taylor Lecture No. 5) (1982)

4   *Radiation Protection and New Medical Diagnostic Procedures,* Proceedings of the Eighteenth Annual Meeting, Held on April 6–7, 1982 (Including Taylor Lecture No. 6) (1983)

5   *Environmental Radioactivity,* Proceedings of the Nineteenth Annual Meeting, Held on April 6–7, 1983 (Including Taylor Lecture No. 7) (1984)

6   *Some Issues Important in Developing Basic Radiation Protection Recommendations,* Proceedings of the Twentieth Annual Meeting, Held on April 4–5, 1984 (Including Taylor Lecture No. 8) (1985)

7   *Radioactive Waste,* Proceedings of the Twenty-first Annual Meeting, Held on April 3–4, 1985 (Including Taylor Lecture No. 9) (1986)

8 *Nonionizing Electromagnetic Radiation and Ultrasound,* Proceedings of the Twenty-second Annual Meeting, Held on April 2–3, 1986 (Including Taylor Lecture No. 10) (1988)

9 *New Dosimetry at Hiroshima and Nagasaki and Its Implications for Risk Estimates,* Proceedings of the Twenty-third Annual Meeting, Held on April 5–6, 1987 (Including Taylor Lecture No. 11) (1988).

10 *Radon,* Proceedings of the Twenty-fourth Annual Meeting, Held on March 30–31, 1988 (Including Taylor Lecture No. 12) (1989).

11 *Radiation Protection Today—The NCRP at Sixty Years,* Proceedings of the Twenty-fifth Annual Meeting, Held on April 5–6, 1989 (Including Taylor Lecture No. 13) (1990).

Symposium Proceedings

The Control of Exposure of the Public to Ionizing Radiation in the Event of Accident or Attack, Proceedings of a Symposium held April 27–29, 1981 (1982)

Lauriston S. Taylor Lectures

No.   Title and Author

1 *The Squares of the Natural Numbers in Radiation Protection* by Herbert M. Parker (1977)

2 *Why be Quantitative About Radiation Risk Estimates?* by Sir Edward Pochin (1978)

3 *Radiation Protection—Concepts and Trade Offs* by Hymer L. Friedell (1979) [Available also in *Perceptions of Risk,* see above]

4 *From "Quantity of Radiation" and "Dose" to "Exposure" and "Absorbed Dose"—An Historical Review* by Harold O. Wyckoff (1980) [Available also in *Quantitative Risks in Standards Setting,* see above]

5 *How Well Can We Assess Genetic Risk? Not Very* by James F. Crow (1981) [Available also in *Critical Issues in Setting Radiation Dose Limits,* see above]

6 *Ethics, Trade-offs and Medical Radiation* by Eugene L. Saenger (1982) [Available also in *Radiation Protection and New Medical Diagnostic Approaches,* see above]

7   *The Human Environment-Past, Present and Future* by Merril Eisenbud (1983) [Available also in *Environmental Radioactivity*, see above]

8   *Limitation and Assessment in Radiation Protection* by Harald H. Rossi (1984) [Available also in *Some Issues Important in Developing Basic Radiation Protection Recommendations*, see above]

9   *Truth (and Beauty) in Radiation Measurement* by John H. Harley (1985) [Available also in *Radioactive Waste*, see above]

10   *Nonionizing Radiation Bioeffects: Cellular Properties and Interactions* by Herman P. Schwan (1986) [Available also in *Nonionizing Electromagnetic Radiations and Ultrasound*, see above]

11   *How to be Quantitative about Radiation Risk Estimates* by Seymour Jablon (1987) [Available also in *New Dosimetry at Hiroshima and Nagasaki and its Implications for Risk Estimates*, see above]

12   *How Safe is Safe Enough?* by Bo Lindell (1988) [Available also in *Radon*, See above]

13   *Radiobiology and Radiation Protection: The Past Century and Prospects for the Future* by Arthur C. Upton (1989) [Available also in *Radiation Protection Today— The NCRP at Sixty Years*, See above]

14   *Radiation Protection and the Internal Emitter Saga* by J. Newell Stannard (1990)

NCRP Commentaries

No.   Title

1   *Krypton-85 in the Atmosphere—With Specific Reference to the Public Health Significance of the Proposed Controlled Release at Three Mile Island* (1980)

2   *Preliminary Evaluation of Criteria for the Disposal of Transuranic Contaminated Waste* (1982)

3   *Screening Techniques for Determining Compliance with Environmental Standards* (1986), Rev. (1989)

4   *Guidelines for the Release of Waste Water from Nuclear Facilities with Special Reference to the Public Health Significance of the Proposed Release of Treated Waste Waters at Three Mile Island* (1987)

5   *Living Without Landfills* (1989)

NCRP Reports

No.   Title

8   *Control and Removal of Radioactive Contamination in
     Laboratories* (1951)

22   *Maximum Permissible Body Burdens and Maximum Per-
     missible Concentrations of Radionuclides in Air and
     in Water for Occupational Exposure* (1959) [Includes
     Addendum 1 issued in August 1963]

23   *Measurement of Neutron Flux and Spectra for Physical
     and Biological Applications* (1960)

25   *Measurement of Absorbed Dose of Neutrons and Mixtures
     of Neutrons and Gamma Rays* (1961)

27   *Stopping Powers for Use with Cavity Chambers* (1961)

30   *Safe Handling of Radioactive Materials* (1964)

32   *Radiation Protection in Educational Institutions* (1966)

35   *Dental X-Ray Protection* (1970)

36   *Radiation Protection in Veterinary Medicine* (1970)

37   *Precautions in the Management of Patients Who Have
     Received Therapeutic Amounts of Radionuclides* (1970)

38   *Protection Against Neutron Radiation* (1971)

40   *Protection Against Radiation from Brachytherapy
     Sources* (1972)

41   *Specifications of Gamma-Ray Brachytherapy Sources*
     (1974)

42   *Radiological Factors Affecting Decision-Making in a
     Nuclear Attack* (1974)

44   *Krypton-85 in the Atmosphere—Accumulation, Biologi-
     cal Significance, and Control Technology* (1975)

46   *Alpha-Emitting Particles in Lungs* (1975)

47   *Tritium Measurement Techniques* (1976)

49   *Structural Shielding Design and Evaluation for Medical
     Use of X Rays and Gamma Rays of Energies Up to 10
     MeV* (1976)

50   *Environmental Radiation Measurements* (1976)

51   *Radiation Protection Design Guidelines for 0.1–100 MeV
     Particle Accelerator Facilities* (1977)

52   *Cesium-137 from the Environment to Man: Metabolism
     and Dose* (1977)

53   *Review of NCRP Radiation Dose Limit for Embryo and
     Fetus in Occupationally Exposed Women* (1977)

54   *Medical Radiation Exposure of Pregnant and Potentially
     Pregnant Women* (1977)

55   *Protection of the Thyroid Gland in the Event of Releases of Radioiodine* (1977)

57   *Instrumentation and Monitoring Methods for Radiation Protection* (1978)

58   *A Handbook of Radioactivity Measurements Procedures, 2nd ed.* (1985)

59   *Operational Radiation Safety Program* (1978)

60   *Physical, Chemical, and Biological Properties of Radiocerium Relevant to Radiation Protection Guidelines* (1978)

61   *Radiation Safety Training Criteria for Industrial Radiography* (1978)

62   *Tritium in the Environment* (1979)

63   *Tritium and Other Radionuclide Labeled Organic Compounds Incorporated in Genetic Material* (1979)

64   *Influence of Dose and Its Distribution in Time on Dose-Response Relationships for Low-LET Radiations* (1980)

65   *Management of Persons Accidentally Contaminated with Radionuclides* (1980)

66   *Mammography* (1980)

67   *Radiofreqency Electromagnetic Fields—Properties, Quantities and Units, Biophysical Interaction, and Measurements* (1981)

68   *Radiation Protection in Pediatric Radiology* (1981)

69   *Dosimetry of X-Ray and Gamma-Ray Beams for Radiation Therapy in the Energy Range 10 keV to 50 MeV* (1981)

70   *Nuclear Medicine—Factors Influencing the Choice and Use of Radionuclides in Diagnosis and Therapy* (1982)

71   *Operational Radiation Safety—Training* (1983)

72   *Radiation Protection and Measurement for Low Voltage Neutron Generators* (1983)

73   *Protection in Nuclear Medicine and Ultrasound Diagnostic Procedures in Children* (1983)

74   *Biological Effects of Ultrasound: Mechanisms and Clinical Implications* (1983)

75   *Iodine-129: Evaluation of Releases from Nuclear Power Generation* (1983)

76   *Radiological Assessment: Predicting the Transport, Bioaccumulation, and Uptake by Man of Radionuclides Released to the Environment* (1984)

77   *Exposures from the Uranium Series with Emphasis on Radon and its Daughters* (1984)

103 *Control of Radon in Houses* (1989)
104 *The Relative Biological Effectiveness of Radiations of Different Qualities* (1990)
105 *Radiation Protection for Medical and Allied Health Personnel* (1989)
106 *Limits of Exposure to "Hot Particles" on the skin* (1989)
107 *Implementation of the Principle of As Low As Reasonably Achievable (ALARA) For Medical and Dental Personnel* (1990)

Binders for NCRP Reports are available. Two sizes make it possible to collect into small binders the "old series" of reports (NCRP Reports Nos. 8–30) and into large binders the more recent publications (NCRP Reports Nos. 32–107). Each binder will accommodate from five to seven reports. The binders carry the identification "NCRP Reports" and come with label holders which permit the user to attach labels showing the reports contained in each binder.

The following bound sets of NCRP Reports are also available:

Volume I. NCRP Reports Nos. 8, 22
Volume II. NCRP Reports Nos. 23, 25, 27, 30
Volume III. NCRP Reports Nos. 32, 35, 36, 37
Volume IV. NCRP Reports Nos. 38, 40, 41
Volume V. NCRP Reports Nos. 42, 44, 46
Volume VI. NCRP Reports Nos. 47, 49, 50, 51
Volume VII. NCRP Reports Nos. 52, 53, 54, 55, 57
Volume VIII. NCRP Reports No. 58
Volume IX. NCRP Reports Nos. 59, 60, 61, 62, 63
Volume X. NCRP Reports Nos. 64, 65, 66, 67
Volume XI. NCRP Reports Nos. 68, 69, 70, 71, 72
Volume XII. NCRP Reports Nos. 73, 74, 75, 76
Volume XIII. NCRP Reports Nos. 77, 78, 79, 80
Volume XIV. NCRP Reports Nos. 81, 82, 83, 84, 85
Volume XV. NCRP Reports Nos. 86, 87, 88, 89
Volume XVI. NCRP Reports Nos. 90, 91, 92, 93
Volume XVII. NCRP Reports Nos. 94, 95, 96, 97
Volume XVIII. NCRP Reports Nos. 98, 99, 100

(Titles of the individual reports contained in each volume are given above).

The following NCRP Reports are now superseded and/or out of print:

No.	Title
1	*X-Ray Protection* (1931). [Superseded by NCRP Report No. 3]
2	*Radium Protection* (1934). [Superseded by NCRP Report No. 4]
3	*X-Ray Protection* (1936). [Superseded by NCRP Report No. 6]
4	*Radium Protection* (1938). [Superseded by NCRP Report No. 13]
5	*Safe Handling of Radioactive Luminous Compounds* (1941). [Out of Print]
6	*Medical X-Ray Protection Up to Two Million Volts* (1949). [Superseded by NCRP Report No. 18]
7	*Safe Handling of Radioactive Isotopes* (1949). [Superseded by NCRP Report No. 30]
9	*Recommendations for Waste Disposal of Phosphorus-32 and Iodine-131 for Medical Users* (1951). [Out of Print]
10	*Radiological Monitoring Methods and Instruments* (1952). [Superseded by NCRP Report No. 57]
11	*Maximum Permissible Amounts of Radioisotopes in the Human Body and Maximum Permissible Concentrations in Air and Water* (1953). [Superseded by NCRP Report No. 22]
12	*Recommendations for the Disposal of Carbon-14 Wastes* (1953). [Superseded by NCRP Report No. 81]
13	*Protection Against Radiations from Radium, Cobalt-60 and Cesium-137* (1954). [Superseded by NCRP Report No. 24]
14	*Protection Against Betatron—Synchrotron Radiations Up to 100 Million Electron Volts* (1954). [Superseded by NCRP Report No. 51]
15	*Safe Handling of Cadavers Containing Radioactive Isotopes* (1953). [Superseded by NCRP Report No. 21]
16	*Radioactive Waste Disposal in the Ocean* (1954). [Out of Print]
17	*Permissible Dose from External Sources of Ionizing Radiation* (1954) including *Maximum Permissible Exposure to Man, Addendum to National Bureau of Standards Handbook 59* (1958). [Superseded by NCRP Report No. 39]
18	*X-Ray Protection* (1955). [Superseded by NCRP Report No. 26]
19	*Regulation of Radiation Exposure by Legislative Means* (1955). [Out of Print]

20   *Protection Against Neutron Radiation Up to 30 Million
       Electron Volts* (1957). [Superseded by NCRP Report
       No. 38]
21   *Safe Handling of Bodies Containing Radioactive Isotopes*
       (1958). [Superseded by NCRP Report No. 37]
24   *Protection Against Radiations from Sealed Gamma
       Sources* (1960). [Superseded by NCRP Report Nos. 33,
       34, and 40]
26   *Medical X-Ray Protection Up to Three Million Volts* (1961).
       [Superseded by NCRP Report Nos. 33, 34, 35, and 36]
28   *A Manual of Radioactivity Procedures* (1961). [Super-
       seded by NCRP Report No. 58]
29   *Exposure to Radiation in an Emergency* (1962). [Super-
       seded by NCRP Report No. 42]
31   *Shielding for High Energy Electron Accelerator Installa-
       tions* (1964). [Superseded by NCRP Report No. 51]
33   *Medical X-Ray and Gamma-Ray Protection for Energies
       up to 10 MeV*—Equipment Design and Use (1968).
       [Superseded by NCRP Report No. 102]
34   *Medical X-Ray and Gamma-Ray Protection for Energies
       Up to 10 MeV—Structural Shielding Design and Eval-
       uation* (1970). [Superseded by NCRP Report No. 49]
39   *Basic Radiation Protection Criteria* (1971). [Superseded
       by NCRP Report No. 91]
43   *Review of the Current State of Radiation Protection Phi-
       losophy* (1975). [Superseded by NCRP Report No. 91]
45   *Natural Background Radiation in the United States*
       (1975). [Superseded by NCRP Report No. 94]
48   *Radiation Protection for Medical and Allied Health Per-
       sonnel* [Superseded by NCRP Report No. 105]
56   *Radiation Exposure from Consumer Products and Miscel-
       laneous Sources* (1977). [Superseded by NCRP Report
       No. 95]
58   *A Handbook on Radioactivity Measurement Procedures.*
       [Superseded by NCRP Report No. 58, 2nd ed.]

Other Documents

The following documents of the NCRP were published outside of
the NCRP Reports and Commentaries series:

"Blood Counts, Statement of the National Committee on Radiation
Protection," Radiology 63, 428 (1954)

"Statements on Maximum Permissible Dose from Television Receivers and Maximum Permissible Dose to the Skin of the Whole Body," Am. J. Roentgenol., Radium Ther. and Nucl. Med. 84, 152 (1960) and Radiology 75, 122 (1960)

Dose Effect Modifying Factors In Radiation Protection, Report of Subcommittee M-4 (Relative Biological Effectiveness) of the National Council on Radiation Protection and Measurements, Report BNL 50073 (T-471) (1967) Brookhaven National Laboratory (National Technical Information Service, Springfield, Virginia).

X-Ray Protection Standards for Home Television Receivers, Interim Statement of the National Council on Radiation Protection and Measurements (National Council on Radiation Protection and Measurements, Washington, 1968)

Specification of Units of Natural Uranium and Natural Thorium (National Council on Radiation Protection and Measurements, Washington, 1973)

NCRP Statement on Dose Limit for Neutrons (National Council on Radiation Protection and Measurements, Washington, 1980)

Control of Air Emissions of Radionuclides (National Council on Radiation Protection and Measurements, Bethesda, Maryland, 1984)

Copies of the statements published in journals may be consulted in libraries. A limited number of copies of the remaining documents listed above are available for distribution by NCRP Publications.

Index

125